A JOURNEY
OF POEMS

A JOURNEY
OF POEMS

EDITED, WITH AN INTRODUCTION AND NOTES,

by RICHARD F. NIEBLING

DELACORTE PRESS, NEW YORK

To George Bennett (1905–1965)

Published by DELL PUBLISHING CO., INC.
750 Third Avenue, New York, N.Y. 10017
Copyright © 1964, Richard F. Niebling
Laurel-Leaf Library ® TM 766734, Dell Publishing Co., Inc.
All rights reserved

Printed in U.S.A.

Second Printing, April 1969

Grateful acknowledgment is made to the following poets, agents and publishers:

"The Unknown Citizen" (Another Time) Copyright 1940 by W. H. Auden. Reprinted from THE COLLECTED POETRY of W. H. Auden, by permission of Random House, Inc., and from COLLECTED SHORTER POEMS by W. H. Auden by permission of Faber and Faber Ltd.

"A Missouri Traveller Writes Home: 1830." Reprinted by permission of Robert Bly.

"London Snow" from THE SHORTER POEMS OF ROBERT BRIDGES. Reprinted by permission of the Clarendon Press.

"The Serf" from ADAMASTOR by Roy Campbell. Reprinted by permission of Curtis Brown Ltd., London.

"Ithaka" by C. P. Cavafy. From SIX POETS OF MODERN GREECE, Edmund Keeley and Philip Sherrard, trans. Copyright © 1960 by Edmund Keeley and Philip Sherrard. Reprinted by permission of Alfred A. Knopf, Inc., and Thames and Hudson, Ltd.

"The Choice" from THE EARLY DROWNED. Copyright © 1961 by Hilary Corke. Reprinted by permission of Martin Secker & Warburg Limited.

"The Long Voyage" from THE DRY SEASON. Copyright 1941 by Malcolm Cowley. Reprinted by permission of the author.

"All but Blind" and "Peace." Reprinted by permission of the Literary Trustees of Walter de la Mare and the Society of Authors as their representative.

"At the Aquarium" from POEMS OF FIVE DECADES by Max Eastman, published by Harper & Row. Reprinted by permission of the author.

"King Juke" and "Travelogue in a Shooting Gallery" from AFTERNOON OF A PAWNBROKER AND OTHER POEMS, copyright 1943 by Kenneth Fearing. Reprinted by permission of Harcourt, Brace & World, Inc., and Ira Koenig, Executor of the Kenneth Fearing Estate.

"Requiem" from NEW AND SELECTED POEMS by Kenneth Fearing. Reprinted by permission of Indiana University Press.

"Pitcher" from THE ORB WEAVER by Robert Francis. Copyright © 1953 by Robert Francis. Reprinted by permission of Wesleyan University Press.

"The Axe-Helve," "An Old Man's Winter Night," and "The Wood-Pile" from THE COMPLETE POEMS OF ROBERT FROST. Copyright 1916, 1923, 1930, 1939 by Holt, Rinehart and Winston, Inc. Copyright 1944, 1951, © 1958 by Robert Frost. Reprinted by permission of Holt, Rinehart and Winston, Inc., and Laurence Pollinger Limited.

"The Sleeping Giant" from EXILES AND MARRIAGES by Donald Hall. Copyright 1955 by Donald Hall. Originally published in THE NEW

contents

introduction

This anthology is, first of all, for the reader who is interested in poetry but whose knowledge of poetry may not be extensive. It offers a collection of poems many of which have not been, or have seldom been, anthologized, and none of which is overly difficult. It juxtaposes poems on similar or related themes, beginning with Cavafy's "Ithaka" and the idea of setting out, and ending with Fearing's "Requiem" and Hardy's "Afterwards." Thus the title —*A Journey of Poems*—a journey to some extent chronological, as the beginning and ending poems suggest, but more significantly, thematic: for this anthology makes a fairly comprehensive canvass of the poet's preoccupations —his love of life and experience in all their variety; his delight in discovery; his awareness of human weakness and social divisiveness; his reaching out with interest and sympathy to his fellow human beings and to the lower creatures with whom he shares the world; his obsession with fate and, overwhelmingly, with time; his love of place; his wish for the good life and an honorable end. These are, of course, the preoccupations of not just the poet but of any thoughtful and sensitive person. This sharing of feelings and ideas, of concerns and meditations will, I believe, justify the approach to poetry by thematic arrangement that this anthology emphasizes.

A Journey of Poems is also for the high school English student who needs poetry above the elementary level but who is not yet ready for either detailed textual analysis or the study of poetry in a chronological scheme. Most of these poems have, in effect, already been chosen by the student, for they are the result of a winnowing out, over a number of years, of poems read by students at Phillips Exeter Academy. Where students were not enthusiastic, or at least puzzled or tantalized, those poems were dropped, not read again. Ultimately a selected group of poems was published at Exeter and used for a couple of years; now, somewhat augmented, it appears in the Laurel-Leaf Library. Nothing is in this book because it is old or because it is famous; most of the poems are of this century; all of them are here because they speak in some way to reasonably "verbal" people of high school age.

As for the teacher who may wish to read these poems with a class, I hope I have left the way clear for him to do as he pleases with them. The thematic arrangement, the logic of which should be clear from the introductions to the twelve sections, is suggestive, not prescriptive; reading the poems in this sequence is one way, but only one way, of using this anthology. Within the sections are groupings of poems sometimes remarkably similar in topic; these may prompt discussion of why a poet has chosen a particular way to communicate, and whether another way would be more or less effective. "Ex-Basketball Player" and "To an Athlete Dying Young"; "The Man with the Hoe" and "The Serf"; the three poems beginning with Michael Thwaites' "The Gull"—such comparisons and others may prove revealing: poem may cast light on poem. One of the delights the true reader constantly experiences is that something he is reading reminds him of something else; the arrangement of poems in *A Journey of Poems* is meant not to stifle this delight, but to stimulate the memory into further search.

Approaches other than the thematic may suggest themselves. Free verse, blank verse, both the Italian and Shakespearean sonnet, many stanzaic devices, even a sestina; narrative, dramatic, lyric, didactic—almost all the forms and types of poetry are here, if emphasis on form or type is desired. But whatever the approach, the important consideration is that the student-reader come to the poems without feeling nagged or bullied, that he talk or write about them with some sense of freedom, and *ultimately try his hand at writing poetry himself.* Pedantic impediments to this experience should be thrust aside. Thus I have not turned this book into a poetry manual; there is, for instance, no glossary of poetic terms, no information on metrics or verse patterns. Such information is readily available elsewhere, and it is best supplied by the teacher anyway, when the student is ready for it, *after* he has begun to get the beat into his head, *after* he sees the poet, searching for form, again and again forge his own verbal chains. Nor have I tagged each poem with a list of questions contrived to steer the reader into an interpretation. Such questions, though sometimes of help to teachers, are an evil device for students, for the eye inevitably goes *first* to the questions and *then* to the poem, and the spontaneous response is effectively distracted and distorted. What I have supplied, besides the inevitable index, are two sets of notes: biographical, for those who wish to place and identify the poets, and textual, for those who need help with archaic terms and remote allusions.

For many students, reading poetry is no problem; for others, the teacher has his work cut out for him. How shall he overcome reluctance and recalcitrance, remove the prejudice that poetry is "flowery" and effete, thwart and redirect the desperate search for "deep" meanings that are not there, budge the literalness that mutters, "Why does he have to say it that way?" I can only suggest not to take poetry too seriously, not, for example, to turn it into a store of knowledge to be learned. And I think none of us English teachers capitalizes enough on the basic interest in words that nearly everyone has. A poem is a verbal contraption; writing poetry has affinities with the construction of crossword puzzles and double-crostics, with the playing of anagrams or scrabble. *Bouts-rimés,* sonnets without the rhyme-words, stanzas with lines omitted—such techniques are legitimate ways of moving students toward the poetic. And as for the student clinging to the security of prose—the *prosaic* student—I suggest that, in default of a radical rearrangement of his genes, there may be ways of loosening his grasp. Let him compare the

evening weather report—"Good evening. This is your
Channel Blank meteorologist. The wind outside our studio
is averaging a steady 8–10 miles an hour; the temperature
is 75°; the barometer is 29.87 and rising; the sky is clear"
—with the opening stanza of Lionel Johnson's "By the
Statue of King Charles." Or let him compare John Muir's
prose description and William Matchett's poetic description of the same bird. It is just possible that he may become something more than an expert on water ouzels.

I acknowledge my indebtedness to my colleagues, most
particularly James Moffett, William Schwarz, and Alan
Vrooman, who cooperated so willingly in my "poetry
project"; and to George Bennett, whose encouragement
and active assistance have been indispensable and who
has been with me from the beginning in the search for
better poems for boys at Exeter.

—*Richard F. Niebling*
Phillips Exeter Academy

section one.

The great life is a journey, never ended till death,
"full of adventure, full of instruction." Curiosity,
love of experience for its own sake, joy in discovery
are here celebrated by the poets.

ITHAKA[1]

When you set out for Ithaka
ask that your way be long,
full of adventure, full of instruction.
The Laistrygonians[2] and the Cyclops,
angry Poseidon—do not fear them:
such as these you will never find
as long as your thought is lofty, as long as a rare
emotion touch your spirit and your body.
The Laistrygonians and the Cyclops,[3]
angry Poseidon—you will not meet them
unless you carry them in your soul,   10
unless your soul raise them up before you.

Ask that your way be long.
At many a summer dawn to enter
—with what gratitude, what joy—
ports seen for the first time;
to stop at Phoenician trading centres,
and to buy good merchandise,
mother of pearl and coral, amber and ebony,
and sensuous perfumes of every kind,
sensuous perfumes as lavishly as you can;   20
to visit many Egyptian cities,
to gather stores of knowledge from the learned.

Ithaka   **15**

Have Ithaka always in your mind.
Your arrival there is what you are destined for.
But do not in the least hurry the journey.
Better that it last for years,
so that when you reach the island you are old,
rich with all you have gained on the way,
not expecting Ithaka to give you wealth.

Ithaka gave you the splendid journey.   30
Without her you would not have set out.
She hasn't anything else to give you.

And if you find her poor, Ithaka has not deceived you.
So wise have you become, of such experience,
that already you will have understood what these
    Ithakas mean.
                                          —CAVAFY

ULYSSES[1]

It little profits that an idle king,
By this still hearth, among these barren crags,
Matched with an aged wife, I mete and dole
Unequal laws unto a savage race,
That hoard, and sleep, and feed, and know not me.
I cannot rest from travel; I will drink
Life to the lees. All times I have enjoyed
Greatly, have suffered greatly, both with those
That loved me, and alone; on shore, and when
Through scudding drifts the rainy Hyades[2]   10
Vexed the dim sea. I am become a name;
For always roaming with a hungry heart
Much have I seen and known,—cities of men
And manners, climates, councils, governments,
Myself not least, but honored of them all;
And drunk delight of battle with my peers,
Far on the ringing plains of windy Troy.
I am a part of all that I have met;

Ulysses   **16**

Yet all experience is an arch wherethrough
Gleams that untraveled world whose margin fades   20
For ever and for ever when I move.
How dull it is to pause, to make an end,
To rust unburnished, not to shine in use,
As though to breathe were life. Life piled on life
Were all too little, and of one to me
Little remains; but every hour is saved
From that eternal silence, something more,
A bringer of new things; and vile it were
For some three suns to store and hoard myself,
And this gray spirit yearning in desire   30
To follow knowledge like a sinking star,
Beyond the utmost bound of human thought.
    This is my son, mine own Telemachus,
To whom I leave the scepter and the isle—
Well-loved of me, discerning to fulfill
This labor, by slow prudence to make mild
A rugged people, and through soft degrees
Subdue them to the useful and the good.
Most blameless is he, centered in the sphere
Of common duties, decent not to fail   40
In offices of tenderness, and pay
Meet adoration to my household gods,
When I am gone. He works his work, I mine.
    There lies the port; the vessel puffs her sail;
There gloom the dark, broad seas. My mariners,
Souls that have toiled, and wrought, and thought
        with me—
That ever with a frolic welcome took
The thunder and the sunshine, and opposed
Free hearts, free foreheads—you and I are old;
Old age hath yet his honor and his toil;   50
Death closes all—but something ere the end,
Some work of noble note, may yet be done
Not unbecoming men that strove with Gods.
The lights begin to twinkle from the rocks;
The long day wanes; the slow moon climbs; the deep
Moans round with many voices. Come, my friends,

"Tis not too late to seek a newer world.
Push off, and sitting well in order smite
The sounding furrows; for my purpose holds
To sail beyond the sunset, and the baths   60
Of all the western stars, until I die.
It may be that the gulfs will wash us down:
It may be we shall touch the Happy Isles,[3]
And see the great Achilles, whom we knew.
Though much is taken, much abides; and though
We are not now that strength which in old days
Moved earth and heaven, that which we are, we are,
One equal temper of heroic hearts,
Made weak by time and fate, but strong in will
To strive, to seek, to find, and not to yield.   70

—ALFRED LORD TENNYSON

SESTINA OF THE TRAMP-ROYAL

Speakin' in general, I 'ave tried 'em all—
The 'appy roads that take you o'er the world.
Speakin' in general, I 'av found them good
For such as cannot use one bed too long,
But must get 'ence, the same as I 'ave done,
An' go observin' matters till they die.

What do it matter where or 'ow we die,
So long as we've our 'ealth to watch it all—
The different ways that different things are done,
An' men an' women lovin' in this world;   10
Takin' our chances as they come along,
An' when they ain't, pretendin' they are good?

In cash or credit—no, it aren't no good;
You 'ave to 'ave the 'abit or you'd die,
Unless you lived your life but one day long,
Nor didn't prophesy nor fret at all,
But drew your tucker some'ow from the world,
An' never bothered what you might ha' done.

But, Gawd, what things are they I 'aven't done!
I've turned my 'and to most, an' turned it good,   20
In various situations round the world—
For 'im that doth not work must surely die;
But that's no reason man should labor all
'Is life on one same shift—life's none so long.

Therefore, from job to job I've moved along.
Pay couldn't 'old me when my time was done,
For something in my 'ead upset it all,
Till I 'ad dropped whatever 'twas for good,
An' out at sea, be'eld the dock-lights die,
An' met my mate—the wind that tramps the world!   30

It's like a book, I think, this bloomin' world,
Which you can read and care for just so long,
But presently you feel that you will die
Unless you get the page you're readin' done,
An' turn another—likely not so good;
But what you're after is to turn 'em all.

Gawd bless this world; Whatever she 'ath done—
Excep' when awful long—I've found it good.
So write, before I die, ' 'E liked it all!'
                                        —RUDYARD KIPLING

ON FIRST LOOKING
INTO CHAPMAN'S HOMER

Much have I travell'd in the realms of gold,
   And many goodly states and kingdoms seen;
   Round many western islands have I been
Which bards in fealty to Apollo hold.[1]
Oft of one wide expanse had I been told
   That deep-brow'd Homer ruled as his demesne.[2]
   Yet did I never breathe its pure serene
Till I heard Chapman[3] speak out loud and bold:
Then felt I like some watcher of the skies

When a new planet swims into his ken;   10
Or like stout Cortez⁴ when with eagle eyes
   He star'd at the Pacific—and all his men
Look'd at each other with a wild surmise—
   Silent, upon a peak in Darien.

—JOHN KEATS

A MISSOURI TRAVELLER
WRITES HOME: 1830

The spring rides down; from Judith and the Larb,
Straining and full, the choked Missouri, choked
With sticks and roots, and high with floating trees
Rides down, as my mind at this oakwood table.
For May unlocks the Crazy Hills,[1]
Pouring, as she has done before, the shattered snow-
    fields down
Till the rumbling brown has burned the land away
A hundred feet below the plain
With spoils of snowfields from the Crazy Hills.
Day breaks, and the Pawnees on those cliffs   10
Above, shouting, keep pace with us;
The warrior trains like rocks against the sky:
At dawn we see the crumbling cliffs at first,
Then horse and rider, then the Western sky;
Those ash-grey horses black against the clouds!
Tall men, high, fierce, with shoulders as if brass
They lift long warbows made by the Dakotahs,
Above their Pawnee shields of black and white;
With cries and howls, all day they shriek on cliffs.
The buffalo, drinking at the shore, in herds   20
Hear, and shoulders humping, the buffalo stampede
Alarmed, up porch to porch, onto the plains of dust,
And I have heard the buffalo stampede
With muffled clatter of colliding horns.
On the whole, peril hangs above this land
Like smoke that floats at dawn above dead fires.
The Sioux believe all people, scalped or choked,

Are locked out of Paradise, yet I have seen
Small Sioux women hanging from scraggly trees;
On scaffolds stretch the acres of the dead,   30
Corroding in their sepulchres of air; at night
With cries, the Osage from their teepee doors,
Mourn the dead, cutting their arms, and screaming;
At dawn the buzzard flocks awake on trees, dew-
      damp,
And stretch their black wings toward the sun to dry.
Such are the few details that I have seen.

The River splits this country, and it seems
We see the Indians always walking Western banks,
Faced toward full sun, like nephews of the sun;
And there are signs of what will come: the whites,   40
With steel traps hanging, swung from saddle thongs,
Or flat Virginians, behind great round wheels:
All whites believe these Rees and Sioux and Kaws
And Mandans are not men, but damned as beasts:
Are damned; are held knit in damnation now
Like grasp of snakes, in Satan's grasp himself,
And like the serpent's hold, it is by death alone
To be released: The Sioux are still and silent
Generally, and I have watched them stand
By ones and twos upon the river's bank   50
As glum as Hudson's blankets winding them,
While shuttling steamboats smoke, labouring up
The breaking foam, beyond the cottonwoods,
Into the region of their dead and of their youth,
Pushed up, they say, by smoke; and they believe
The tribe of whites, like smoke, soon shall return
From whence it came: and therefore in both minds
The truth is absent; and the hands alone
Are like the willow trees, forever green
And undeceived: the hands continue killing.   60
The hands go on, the minds remain behind,
As if the concepts handled by the mind
Were lesser than the concepts of the hands,
As if a man achieves more than he knows;

A Missouri Traveller Writes Home: 1830   **21**

Or if the pain of action were so great
And life so freezing and Medusa-faced,
That, like Medusa's head,[2] it could be held
And not observed, lest eye's reward be stone.

The night grows old above this river boat.
Before I end, I shall include account   70
Of an incident tonight that moved my wonder.
At dusk we tied the boat to trees on shore;
No mortal boat in these night shoals can live.
At first I heard a cry: shuffling and cries
And muffled sounds on deckoak overhead
Drew me on deck, the air was chill, and there
I sensed, because these senses here are sharp
And must be, something living and unknown.
To night and North a crowd stared from the boatrail,
Upriver, nightward and North: a speck of white.   80
The thing was white: the resonance of night
Returned its grunts and whistlings on the air.
The frontier men swore in that river thicket
In ambush like the beasts they're modeled on,
Bristling for war, would be a thresh of Sioux;
The crew and gamblers nudged, to bait the settlers,
And arms nudged cry, "Along the river there's
Some settler's cow, Hereford or Poland China,
Some farmer could not nail tight enough in cribs,
And terrorizing frogs and catfish now."   90
But Mormons see some robe in that faint white,
In that dim white the angel of death, come
In cottonwoods to sign the Second Coming;
And on the river's border there they see
Some angel of Joseph upon the chill Missouri;
One man believed that there was nothing there,
As the moon too is false, and its white is false.
I sensed a fear, as if the wind protected it.
When the talk died, eight men, and I with them,
Set off, and moving overboard in dark,   100
With guns, protected by the thunder's noise,
Up the dark river, toward where the splashes rose,

A Missouri Traveller Writes Home: 1830   **22**

So armed in case of Sioux, to our surprise
We found a white and wounded Northern Bear,
Shot in that day about the snout and head.
The pure-white bear,[3] not native to these parts,
But to the Horns, or Ranges born, and shot
That morning, had turned downward South and East,
And had apparently through these dry plains
Passed South, to lay its burning paws and head   110
And lay its fever-proud and festered flesh
Within the cool Missouri's turbid bed.
Soon after, clouds of rain drove us indoors,
And lightning fell like sheets upon the sand,
Said to be sudden in these Western lands.
Minutes before it broke, a circling mass
Of split-tail swallows came and then were gone.
But now to bed. We disembark at dawn
And start to westward through the heavy grass.
                                        —ROBERT BLY

section two.

The first two poems in this section show
the adventurous and free imagination of
childhood; the third reveals childhood as a time
more problematical; and the last is about
a family of storytellers and a
childhood recalled.

ROMANCE

When I was but thirteen or so
   I went into a golden land,
Chimborazo, Cotopaxi
   Took me by the hand.

My father died, my brother too,
   They passed like fleeting dreams,
I stood where Popocatapetl [1]
   In the sunlight gleams.

I dimly heard the master's voice
   And boys far-off at play,—
Chimborazo, Cotopaxi
   Had stolen me away.

I walked in a great golden dream
   To and fro from school—
Shining Popocatapetl
   The dusty streets did rule.

I walked home with a gold dark boy
   And never a word I'd say,

10

Chimborazo, Cotopaxi
   Had taken my speech away.   20

I gazed entranced upon his face
   Fairer than any flower—
O shining Popocatapetl
   It was thy magic hour:

The houses, people, traffic seemed
   Thin fading dreams by day;
Chimborazo, Cotopaxi,
   They had stolen my soul away!

                   —W. J. TURNER

THE SLEEPING GIANT
(A Hill, So Named, in Hamden, Connecticut)

The whole day long, under the walking sun
That poised an eye on me from its high floor,
Holding my toy beside the clapboard house
I looked for him, the summer I was four.

I was afraid the waking arm would break
From the loose earth and rub against his eyes
A fist of trees, and the whole country tremble
In the exultant labor of his rise;

Then he with giant steps in the small streets
Would stagger, cutting off the sky, to seize   10
The roofs from house and home because we had
Covered his shape with dirt and planted trees;

And then kneel down and rip with fingernails
A trench to pour the enemy Atlantic
Into our basin, and the water rush,
With the streets full and the voices frantic.

That was the summer I expected him.

The Sleeping Giant   **25**

Later the high and watchful sun instead
Walked low behind the house, and school began,
And winter pulled a sheet over his head.   20
                              —DONALD HALL

ELEVEN

And summer mornings the mute child, rebellious,
Stupid, hating the words, the meanings, hating
The Think now, Think, the O but Think! would leave
On tiptoe the three chairs on the verandah
And crossing tree by tree the empty lawn
Push back the shed door and upon the sill
Stand pressing out the sunlight from his eyes
And enter and with outstretched fingers feel
The grindstone and behind it the bare wall
And turn and in the corner on the cool   10
Hard earth sit listening. And one by one,
Out of the dazzled shadow in the room,
The shapes would gather, the brown plowshare,
    spades,
Mattocks, the polished helves of picks, a scythe
Hung from the rafters, shovels, slender tines
Glinting across the curve of sickles—shapes
Older than men were, the wise tools, the iron
Friendly with earth. And sit there, quiet, breathing
The harsh dry smell of withered bulbs, the faint
Odor of dung, the silence. And outside   20
Beyond the half-shut door the blind leaves
And the corn moving. And at noon would come,
Up from the garden, his hard crooked hands
Gentle with earth, his knees still earth-stained,
    smelling
Of sun, of summer, the old gardener, like
A priest, like an interpreter, and bend
Over his baskets.
                    And they would not speak:

They would say nothing. And the child would sit
    there   30
Happy as though he had no name, as though
He had been no one: like a leaf, a stem,
Like a root growing—

                        —ARCHIBALD MACLEISH

THE SOMERSET DAM FOR SUPPER

She tells us an interminable story, from television,
Through the fried potatoes, hamburg, and coleslaw.
    She is five.
She uses her mother's voice, voices and names from
    school life,
To be the only one talking. Her mother watches me
    for signs of impatience.
I am her father, I conceal my impatience, and for his
    own good
Silence her brother, restless at monologue not his
    own. He is nine.
It ends with only bread left, coffee coming for the
    grownups.

I begin the true story of the long trip to Somerset
    Dam in 1912
With my father, by train from North Cambridge to
    Hoosac Tunnel,
By narrow-gauge to Mountain Mills where log booms
    filled a sawmill lake,   10
By gas car to the bunkhouse end of the line. A berry-
    eating bear
Plunged into the bushes along the tracks. Excite-
    ment. A real bear?
A real bear. What color? Brown, I say, but didn't
    really see.
I am the only one talking, and tell them now about
    the flat-bed wagon

To the engineers' house at the base of the big earth
    dam.
He and she and their mother never heard this story. I
    have more.

But he runs to my desk, brings back a photograph of
    the dam;
Maybe his grandfather's boy, I think, as he turns my
    table story
Into an explanation of the dam's construction, the
    borrow pits,
The dump cars on the bare log trestles. I begin again,   20
Remembering when my father took me, and my sister
    and brother,
To see the steam shovels at the east borrow pit. A
    shouted
Warning, we ducked behind a small rock and a
    forked birch,
And Boom, and Roar, went the dynamite,
Rock raining all around us, but no one hit.
He likes this part. He is nine.

My father was chief engineer—and important, I
    knew, when the foreman,
Helmeted and scared, came running to see if he had
    killed any of us.
But we shouldn't have been there, and my father
    couldn't be angry.
Later my mother said, "What were you thinking of,
    taking the children there?"   30
He had no excuse for that, either. This part is for my
    wife.
I have more story, but no more dynamite. Time for
    ice cream.

Our son's unusual silence has earned him his turn
    now.
He begins a riddle, anything to be talking: There
    were seven pine trees—

The Somerset Dam for Supper   28

His sister says, "Acorns!," and he storms out of the
    room; the giveaway
Ruins it. We all call at once to come back, shut up,
    sit down, stop crying.
The ice cream is brought. He comes back, gets a grip
    on himself, starts again.
I try to multiply seven pine trees times seven
    branches times seven
Twigs on each, times seven acorns on each twig,
    and can't.
None, is the answer. Now he has the center of
    attention. Climax.   40

Time to clear the supper table. The first storyteller
Feels it has been too long since her performance,
    wants to repeat,
But we carry away dishes, and in the kitchen my wife
Washes the glass of the framed photograph of
    Somerset Dam, 1912
(My father's square lettering in Higgins' Black Ink
    for draughtsmen),
And I hang it under a shelf there. None of them
    knows it,
But I intend to tell about the berry-eating bear and
    the dynamite
Again tomorrow, and go on from there.
                         It's a long story,
As I think of the fisherman who, pulling a trout from
    the river,
Snagged a low-flying young hawk for a double catch,   50
And the morning ritual of rain gauge and ther-
    mometer,
And the half-Indian cook who came with a knife to
    collect
What he'd won playing cards with our cook.
                         I'll outtalk them.
I'm the father, and at fifty-six I know more, that's all.
                    —JOHN HOLMES

The Somerset Dam for Supper   **29**

section three.

This section contains poems that emphasize,
in various ways, lives that are impaired and damaged
—poems about inaction, fear, cruelty, pathos, horror
—the unpleasant and dark side of existence.

DAYS

Daughters of Time, the hypocritic Days,
Muffled and dumb like barefoot dervishes,[1]
And marching single in an endless file,
Bring diadems and fagots in their hands.
To each they offer gifts after his will,
Bread, kingdoms, stars, and sky that holds them all.
I, in my pleached garden,[2] watched the pomp,
Forgot my morning wishes, hastily
Took a few herbs and apples, and the Day
Turned and departed silent. I, too late,   10
Under her solemn fillet saw the scorn.
                              —RALPH WALDO EMERSON

THE UNKNOWN CITIZEN
(To JS/07/M/378 This Marble Monument Is Erected
    by the State)

He was found by the Bureau of Statistics to be
One against whom there was no official complaint,
And all the reports on his conduct agree
That, in the modern sense of an old-fashioned word,
    he was a saint,

For in everything he did he served the Greater
  Community.
Except for the War, till the day he retired
He worked in a factory and never got fired,
But satisfied his employers, Fudge Motors Inc.
Yet he wasn't a scab or odd in his views,
For his Union reports that he paid his dues,   10
(Our report on his Union shows it was sound)
And our Social Psychology workers found
That he was popular with his mates and liked a
  drink.
The Press are convinced that he bought a paper every
  day
And that his reactions to advertisements were normal
  in every way.
Policies taken out in his name prove that he was fully
  insured,
And his Health-card shows he was once in hospital
  but left it cured.
Both Producers Research and High-Grade Living
  declare
He was fully sensible to the advantages of the Install-
  ment Plan
And had everything necessary to the Modern Man,   20
A phonograph, a radio, a car and a frigidaire.
Our researchers into Public Opinion are content
That he held the proper opinions for the time of year;
When there was peace, he was for peace; when there
  was war, he went.
He was married and added five children to the
  population,
Which our Eugenist says was the right number for
  a parent of his generation,
And our teachers report that he never interfered with
  their education.
Was he free? Was he happy? The question is absurd:
Had anything been wrong, we should certainly have
  heard.

—W. H. AUDEN

THE LEADEN-EYED

Let not young souls be smothered out before
They do quaint deeds and fully flaunt their pride.
It is the world's one crime its babes grow dull,
Its poor are oxlike, limp, and leaden-eyed.
Not that they starve, but starve so dreamlessly,
Not that they sow, but that they seldom reap,
Not that they serve, but have no gods to serve;
Not that they die, but that they die like sheep.

—VACHEL LINDSAY

EX-BASKETBALL PLAYER

Pearl Avenue runs past the high school lot,
Bends with the trolley tracks, and stops, cut off
Before it has a chance to go two blocks,
At Colonel McComsky Plaza. Berth's Garage
Is on the corner facing west, and there,
Most days, you'll find Flick Webb, who helps Berth
    out.

Flick stands tall among the idiot pumps—
Five on a side, the old bubble-head style,
Their rubber elbows hanging loose and low.
One's nostrils are two S's, and his eyes   10
An E and O. And one is squat, without
A head at all—more of a football type.

Once, Flick played for the high school team, the
    Wizards.
He was good: in fact, the best. In '46,
He bucketed three hundred ninety points,
A county record still. The ball loved Flick.
I saw him rack up thirty-eight or forty
In one home game. His hands were like wild birds.

Ex-Basketball Player   **32**

He never learned a trade; he just sells gas,
Checks oil, and changes flats. Once in a while,   20
As a gag, he dribbles an inner tube,
But most of us remember anyway.
His hands are fine and nervous on the lug wrench.
It makes no difference to the lug wrench, though.

Off work, he hangs around Mae's Luncheonette.
Grease-grey and kind of coiled, he plays pinball,
Sips lemon cokes, and smokes those thin cigars;
Flick seldom speaks to Mae, just sits and nods
Beyond her face towards bright applauding tiers
Of Necco Wafers, Nibs, and Juju Beads.   30

—JOHN UPDIKE

TO AN ATHLETE DYING YOUNG

The time you won your town the race
We chaired you through the marketplace;
Man and boy stood cheering by,
And home we brought you shoulder-high.

Today, the road all runners come,
Shoulder-high we bring you home,
And set you at your threshold down,
Townsman of a stiller town.

Smart lad, to slip betimes away
From fields where glory does not stay,   10
And early though the laurel grows,
It withers quicker than the rose.

Eyes the shady night has shut
Cannot see the record cut,
And silence sounds no worse than cheers
After earth has stopped the ears:

Now you will not swell the rout

Of lads that wore their honours out,
Runners whom renown outran
And the name died before the man.

So set, before its echoes fade,
The fleet foot on the sill of shade,
And hold to the low lintel up
The still-defended challenge-cup.

And round that early-laurelled head
Will flock to gaze the strengthless dead,
And find unwithered on its curls
The garland briefer than a girl's.

—A. E. HOUSMAN

THE SHELL

I.
And then I pressed the shell
Close to my ear,
And listened well.

And straightway, like a bell,
Came low and clear
The slow, sad murmur of far distant seas,

Whipped by an icy breeze
Upon a shore
Windswept and desolate.

It was a sunless strand that never bore   10
The footprint of a man,
Nor felt the weight

Since time began
Of any human quality or stir,
Save what the dreary winds and waves incur.

II.

And in the hush of waters was the sound
Of pebbles, rolling round;
Forever rolling, with a hollow sound:

And bubbling seaweeds, as the waters go,
Swish to and fro   20
Their long cold tentacles of slimy grey;

There was no day;
Nor ever came a night
Setting the stars alight

To wonder at the moon:
Was twilight only, and the frightened croon,
Smitten to whimpers, of the dreary wind

And waves that journeyed blind . . .
And then I loosed my ear.—Oh, it was sweet
To hear a cart go jolting down the street!   30

—JAMES STEPHENS

IN WASTE PLACES

As a naked man I go
Through the desert, sore afraid;
Holding high my head, although
I'm as frightened as a maid.

The lion crouches there! I saw
In barren rocks his amber eye!
He parts the cactus with his paw!
He stares at me as I go by!

He would pad upon my trace
If he thought I was afraid!   10

In Waste Places   **35**

If he knew my hardy face
Veils the terrors of a maid.

He rises in the nighttime, and
He stretches forth! He snuffs the air!
He roars! He leaps along the sand!
He creeps! He watches everywhere!

His burning eyes, his eyes of bale
Through the darkness I can see!
He lashes fiercely with his tail!
He makes again to spring at me!   20

I am the lion, and his lair!
I am the fear that frightens me!
I am the desert of despair!
And the night of agony!

Night or day, whate'er befall,
I must walk that desert land,
Until I dare my fear and call
The lion out to lick my hand.

—JAMES STEPHENS

PORPHYRIA'S LOVER

The rain set early in tonight,
    The sullen wind was soon awake,
It tore the elm-tops down for spite,
    And did its worst to vex the lake:
    I listened with heart fit to break.
When glided in Porphyria; straight
    She shut the cold out and the storm,
And kneeled and made the cheerless grate
    Blaze up, and all the cottage warm;
    Which done, she rose, and from her form   10
Withdrew the dripping cloak and shawl,
    And laid her soiled gloves by, untied

Her hat and let the damp hair fall,
    And, last, she sat down by my side
    And called me. When no voice replied,
She put my arm about her waist,
    And made her smooth white shoulder bare,
And all her yellow hair displaced,
    And, stooping, made my cheek lie there,
    And spread o'er all her yellow hair,   20
Murmuring how she loved me—she
    Too weak, for all her heart's endeavour,
To set its struggling passion free
    From pride, and vainer ties dissever,
    And give herself to me for ever.
But passion sometimes would prevail,
    Nor could tonight's gay feast restrain
A sudden thought of one so pale
    For love of her, and all in vain:
    So, she was come through wind and rain.   30
Be sure I looked up at her eyes
    Happy and proud; at last I knew
Porphyria worshipped me; surprise
    Made my heart swell, and still it grew
    While I debated what to do.
That moment she was mine, mine, fair,
    Perfectly pure and good: I found
A thing to do, and all her hair
    In one long yellow string I wound
Three times her little throat around,   40
And strangled her. No pain felt she;
    I am quite sure she felt no pain.
As a shut bud that holds a bee,
    I warily oped her lids: again
    Laughed the blue eyes without a stain.
And I untightened next the tress
    About her neck; her cheek once more
Blushed bright beneath my burning kiss:
    I propped her head up as before,
Only this time my shoulder bore   50

Her head, which droops upon it still:
   The smiling rosy little head,
So glad it has its utmost will,
   That all it scorned at once is fled,
   And I, its love, am gained instead!
Porphyria's love: she guessed not how
   Her darling one wish would be heard.
And thus we sit together now,
   And all night long we have not stirred,
   And yet God has not said a word!   60

                 —ROBERT BROWNING

THE LABORATORY
Ancien Régime

Now that I, tying thy glass mask tightly,
May gaze thro' these faint smokes curling whitely,
As thou pliest thy trade in this devil's-smithy—
Which is the poison to poison her, prithee?

He is with her; and they know that I know
Where they are, what they do: they believe my tears
    flow
While they laugh, laugh at me, at me fled to the drear
Empty church, to pray God in, for them!—I am here.

Grind away, moisten and mash up thy paste,
Pound at thy powder,—I am not in haste!   10
Better sit thus, and observe thy strange things,
Than go where men wait me and dance at the King's.

That in the mortar—you call it a gum?
Ah, the brave tree whence such gold oozings come!
And yonder soft phial, the exquisite blue,
Sure to taste sweetly,—is that poison too?

Had I but all of them, thee and thy treasures,
What a wild crowd of invisible pleasures!

To carry pure death in an earring, a casket,
A signet, a fan-mount, a fillagree basket!   20

Soon, at the King's, a mere lozenge to give,
And Pauline should have just thirty minutes to live!
But to light a pastile, and Elise, with her head
And her breast and her arms and her hands, should
        drop dead!

Quick—is it finished? The colour's too grim!
Why not soft like the phial's, enticing and dim?
Let it brighten her drink, let her turn it and stir,
And try it and taste, ere she fix and prefer!

What a drop! She's not little, no minion like me!
That's why she ensnared him: this never will free   30
The soul from those masculine eyes,—say, "no!"
To that pulse's magnificent come-and-go.

For only last night, as they whispered, I brought
My own eyes to bear on her so, that I thought
Could I keep them one half minute fixed, she would
        fall,
Shrivelled; she fell not; yet this does it all!

Not that I bid you spare her the pain!
Let death be felt and the proof remain:
Brand, burn up, bite into its grace—
He is sure to remember her dying face!   40

Is it done? Take my mask off! Nay, be not morose;
It kills her, and this prevents seeing it close:
The delicate droplet, my whole fortune's fee—
If it hurts her, beside, can it ever hurt me?

Now, take all my jewels, gorge gold to your fill,
You may kiss me, old man, on my mouth if you will!
But brush this dust off me, lest horror it brings
Ere I know it—next moment I dance at the King's!
                                    —ROBERT BROWNING

The Laboratory   39

MY LAST DUCHESS

Ferrara

That's my last Duchess painted on the wall,
Looking as if she were alive. I call
That piece a wonder, now: Fra[1] Pandolf's hands
Worked busily a day, and there she stands.
Will't please you sit and look at her? I said
"Fra Pandolf" by design, for never read
Strangers like you that pictured countenance,
The depth and passion of its earnest glance,
But to myself they turned (since none puts by
The curtain I have drawn for you, but I)   10
And seemed as they would ask me, if they durst,
How such a glance came there; so, not the first
Are you to turn and ask thus. Sir, 'twas not
Her husband's presence only, called that spot
Of joy into the Duchess' cheek: perhaps
Fra Pandolf chanced to say, "Her mantle laps
Over my lady's wrist too much," or "Paint
Must never hope to reproduce the faint
Half-flush that dies along her throat": such stuff
Was courtesy, she thought, and cause enough   20
For calling up that spot of joy. She had
A heart—how shall I say?—too soon made glad,
Too easily impressed; she liked whate'er
She looked on, and her looks went everywhere.
Sir, 'twas all one! My favour at her breast,
The dropping of the daylight in the West,
The bough of cherries some officious fool
Broke in the orchard for her, the white mule
She rode with round the terrace—all and each
Would draw from her alike the approving speech,   30
Or blush, at least. She thanked men,—good! but
      thanked
Somehow—I know not how—as if she ranked
My gift of a nine-hundred-years-old name

With anybody's gift. Who'd stoop to blame
This sort of trifling? Even had you skill
In speech—(which I have not)—to make your will
Quite clear to such an one, and say, "Just this
Or that in you disgusts me; here you miss,
Or there exceed the mark"—and if she let
Herself be lessoned so, nor plainly set   40
Her wits to yours, forsooth, and made excuse,
—E'en then would be some stooping; and I choose
Never to stoop. Oh sir, she smiled, no doubt,
Whene'er I passed her; but who passed without
Much the same smile? This grew; I gave commands;
Then all smiles stopped together. There she stands
As if alive. Will't please you rise? We'll meet
The company below, then. I repeat,
The Count your master's known munificence
Is ample warrant that no just pretence   50
Of mine for dowry will be disallowed;
Though his fair daughter's self, as I avowed
At starting, is my object. Nay, we'll go
Together down, sir. Notice Neptune, though,
Taming a sea-horse, thought a rarity,
Which Claus of Innsbruck cast in bronze for me!

—ROBERT BROWNING

THE HAYSTACK IN THE FLOODS

Had she come all the way for this,
To part at last without a kiss?
Yea, had she borne the dirt and rain
That her own eyes might see him slain
Beside the haystack in the floods?

Along the dripping, leafless woods,
The stirrup touching either shoe,
She rode astride as troopers do;
With kirtle kilted² to her knee,
To which the mud splash'd wretchedly;   10

And the wet dripp'd from every tree
Upon her head and heavy hair,
And on her eyelids broad and fair;
The tears and rain ran down her face.

By fits and starts they rode apace,
And very often was his place
Far off from her; he had to ride
Ahead to see what might betide
When the roads cross'd; and sometimes, when
There rose a murmuring from his men,   20
Had to turn back with promises.
Ah me! she had but little ease;
And often for pure doubt and dread
She sobb'd, made giddy in the head
By the swift riding; while, for cold,
Her slender fingers scarce could hold
The wet reins; yea, and scarcely, too,
She felt the foot within her shoe
Against the stirrup: all for this,   30
To part at last without a kiss
Beside the haystack in the floods.

For when they near'd that old soak'd hay,
They saw across the only way
That Judas, Godmar, and the three
Red running lions dismally
Grinn'd from his pennon, under which,
In one straight line along the ditch,
They counted thirty heads.

                    So then,
While Robert turn'd round to his men,   40
She saw at once the wretched end,
And, stooping down, tried hard to rend
Her coif³ the wrong way from her head,
And hid her eyes; while Robert said:
"Nay, love, 'tis scarcely two to one,
At Poictiers where we made them run

So fast—why, sweet my love, good cheer.
The Gascon frontier[4] is so near,
Nought after this."

           But, "O," she said,
"My God! my God! I have to tread
The long way back without you; then   50
The court at Paris; those six men;[5]
The gratings of the Chatelet;
The swift Seine on some rainy day
Like this, and people standing by,
And laughing, while my weak hands try
To recollect how strong men swim.
All this, or else a life with him,
For which I should be damned at last.
Would God that this next hour were past!"

He answer'd not, but cried his cry,   60
"St. George[6] for Marny!" cheerily;
And laid his hand upon her rein.
Alas! no man of all his train
Gave back that cheery cry again;
And, while for rage his thumb beat fast
Upon his sword-hilts, some one cast
About his neck a kerchief long,
And bound him.

           Then they went along
To Godmar; who said: "Now, Jehane,
Your lover's life is on the wane   70
So fast, that, if this very hour
You yield not as my paramour,
He will not see the rain leave off—
Nay, keep your tongue from gibe and scoff,
Sir Robert, or I slay you now."

She laid her hand upon her brow,
Then gazed upon the palm, as though
She thought her forehead bled, and—"No!"

The Haystack in the Floods   **43**

She said, and turn'd her head away,
As there were nothing else to say,
And everything were settled: red
Grew Godmar's face from chin to head:
"Jehane, on yonder hill there stands
My castle, guarding well my lands:
What hinders me from taking you
And doing that I list to do
To your fair wilful body, while
Your knight lies dead?"

        A wicked smile
Wrinkled her face, her lips grew thin,
A long way out she thrust her chin:
"You know that I should strangle you
While you were sleeping; or bite through
Your throat, by God's help—ah!" she said,
"Lord Jesus, pity your poor maid!
For in such wise they hem me in,
I cannot choose but sin and sin,
Whatever happens: yet I think
They could not make me eat or drink
And so should I just reach my rest."

"Nay, if you do not my behest,
O Jehane! though I love you well,"
Said Godmar, "would I fail to tell
All that I know?" "Foul lies," she said.
"Eh? lies, my Jehane? by God's head,
At Paris folks would deem them true!
Do you know, Jehane, they cry for you,
'Jehane the brown! Jehane the brown!
Give us Jehane to burn or drown!'—
Eh!—gag me Robert!—sweet my friend,
This were indeed a piteous end
For those long fingers, and long feet,
And long neck, and smooth shoulders sweet;
An end that few men would forget
That saw it—So, an hour yet:

The Haystack in the Floods   **44**

80

90

100

110

Consider, Jehane, which to take
Of life or death!"

               So, scarce awake,
Dismounting, did she leave that place,
And totter some yards: with her face
Turn'd upward to the sky she lay,
Her head on a wet heap of hay,   120
And fell asleep: and while she slept,
And did not dream, the minutes crept
Round to the twelve again; but she,
Being waked at last, sigh'd quietly,
And strangely childlike came, and said:
"I will not." Straightway Godmar's head,
As though it hung on strong wires, turn'd
Most sharply round, and his face burn'd.

For Robert—both his eyes were dry,
He could not weep, but gloomily   130
He seem'd to watch the rain; yea, too,
His lips were firm; he tried once more
To touch her lips; she reach'd out, sore
And vain desire so tortured them,
The poor grey lips, and now the hem
Of his sleeve brush'd them.

                    With a start
Up Godmar rose, thrust them apart;
From Robert's throat he loosed the bands
Of silk and mail; with empty hands
Held out, she stood and gazed and saw   140
The long bright blade without a flaw
Glide out from Godmar's sheath, his hand
In Robert's hair; she saw him bend
Back Robert's head; she saw him send
The thin steel down; the blow told well—
Right backward the knight Robert fell,
And moan'd as dogs do, being half dead,
Unwitting, as I deem: so then

Godmar turn'd grinning to his men,
Who ran, some five or six, and beat   150
His head to pieces at their feet.

Then Godmar turn'd again and said:
"So, Jehane, the first fitte[7] is read!
Take note, my lady, that your way
Lies backward to the Chatelet!"
She shook her head and gazed awhile
At her cold hands with a rueful smile,
As though this thing had made her mad.

This was the parting that they had
Beside the haystack in the floods.   160
                                        —WILLIAM MORRIS

THE REVENGE OF HAMISH

It was three slim does and a ten-tined [1] buck in the
    bracken[2] lay;
    And all of a sudden the sinister smell of a man,
    Awaft on a wind-shift, wavered and ran
Down the hillside and sifted along through the
    bracken and passed that way.

Then Nan got a-tremble at nostril; she was the dain-
    tiest doe;
    In the print of her velvet flank on the velvet fern
    She reared, and rounded her ears in turn.
Then the buck leapt up, and his head as a king's to
    a crown did go

Full high in the breeze, and he stood as if Death had
    the form of a deer;
    And the two slim does long lazily stretching arose,   10
    For their daydream slowlier came to a close,
Till they woke and were still, breath-bound with wait-
    ing and wonder and fear.

Then Alan the huntsman sprang over the hillock, the
    hounds shot by,
    The does and the ten-tined buck made a marvellous
        bound,
    The hounds swept after with never a sound,
But Alan loud winded his horn in sign that the quarry
    was nigh.

For at dawn of that day proud Maclean of Lochbuy
    to the hunt had waxed wild,
    And he cursed at old Alan till Alan fared off with
        the hounds
    For to drive him the deer to the lower glen-
        grounds:
"I will kill a red deer," quoth Maclean, "in the sight
    of the wife and the child."   20

So gayly he paced with the wife and the child to his
    chosen stand;
    But he hurried tall Hamish the henchman ahead:
        "Go turn"—
    Cried Maclean—"if the deer seek to cross to the
        burn,[3]
Do thou turn them to me: nor fail, lest thy back be
    as red as thy hand."

Now hard-fortuned Hamish, half blown of his breath
    with the height of the hill,
    Was white in the face when the ten-tined buck and
        the does
    Drew leaping to burn-ward; huskily rose
His shouts, and his nether lip twitched, and his legs
    were o'er-weak for his will.

So the deer darted lightly by Hamish and bounded
    away to the burn.
    But Maclean never bating[4] his watch tarried
        waiting below;   30
    Still Hamish hung heavy with fear for to go

All the space of an hour; then he went, and his face
    was greenish and stern,

And his eye sat back in the socket, and shrunken the
    eye-balls shone,
    As withdrawn from a vision of deeds it were shame
        to see.
    "Now, now, grim henchman, what is't with thee?"
Brake Maclean, and his wrath rose red as a beacon
    the wind hath upblown.

"Three does and a ten-tined buck made out," spoke
    Hamish, full mild,
    "And I ran for to turn, but my breath it was blown,
        and they passed;
    I was weak, for ye called ere I broke me my fast."
Cried Maclean: "Now a ten-tined buck in the sight of
    the wife and the child   40

I had killed if the gluttonous kern [5] had not wrought
    me a snail's own wrong!"
    Then he sounded, and down came kinsmen and
        clansmen all:
    "Ten blows, for ten tine, on his back let fall,
And reckon no stroke if the blood follow not at the
    bite of the thong!"

So Hamish made bare, and took him his strokes; at
    the last he smiled.
    "Now I'll to the burn," quoth Maclean, "for it still
        may be,
    If a slimmer-paunched henchman will hurry with
        me,
I shall kill me the ten-tined buck for a gift to the
    wife and the child!"

Then the clansmen departed, by this path and that;
    and over the hill

Sped Maclean with an outward wrath for an in-
ward shame;
And that place of the lashing full quiet became;
And the wife and the child stood sad; and bloody-
backed Hamish sat still.

But look! red Hamish has risen; quick about and
about turns he.
"There is none betwixt me and the crag-top!" he
screams under breath.
Then, livid as Lazarus lately from death,
He snatches the child from the mother, and clambers
the crag toward the sea.

Now the mother drops breath; she is dumb, and her
heart goes dead for a space,
Till the motherhood, mistress of death, shrieks,
shrieks through the glen,
And that place of the lashing is live with men,
And Maclean, and the gillie [6] that told him, dash up
in a desperate race.

Not a breath's time for asking; an eye-glance reveals
all the tale untold.
They follow mad Hamish afar up the crag toward
the sea,
And the lady cries: "Clansmen, run for a fee!—
Yon castle and lands to the first two hands that shall
hook him and hold

Fast Hamish back from the brink!"—and ever she
flies up the steep,
And the clansmen pant, and they sweat, and they
jostle and strain.
But mother, 'tis vain; but, father, 'tis vain;
Stern Hamish stands bold on the brink, and dangles
the child o'er the deep.

The Revenge of Hamish   **49**

Now a faintness falls on the men that run, and they
all stand still.
And the wife prays Hamish as if he were God,
on her knees,   70
Crying: "Hamish! O Hamish! but please, but please
For to spare him!" and Hamish still dangles the child,
with a wavering will.

On a sudden he turns; with a sea-hawk scream, and a
gibe, and a song,
Cries: "So; I will spare ye the child if, in sight of
ye all,
Ten blows on Maclean's bare back shall fall,
And ye reckon no stroke if the blood follow not at the
bite of the thong!"

Then Maclean he set hardly his tooth to his lip that
his tooth was red,
Breathed short for a space, said: "Nay, but it never
shall be!
Let me hurl off the damnable hound in the sea!"
But the wife: "Can Hamish go fish us the child from
the sea, if dead?   80

"Say yea!—Let them lash me, Hamish?"—"Nay!"—
"Husband, the lashing will heal;
But, oh, who will heal me the bonny sweet bairn'
in his grave?
Could ye cure me my heart with the death of a
knave?
Quick, Love! I will bare thee—so—kneel!" Then
Maclean 'gan slowly to kneel

With never a word, till presently downward he jerked
to the earth.
Then the henchman—he that smote Hamish—
would tremble and lag;
"Strike, hard!" quoth Hamish, full stern, from the
crag;

The Revenge of Hamish   50

Then he struck him, and "One!" sang Hamish, and
  danced with the child in his mirth.

And no man spake beside Hamish; he counted each
  stroke with a song.
  When the last stroke fell, then he moved him a
    pace down the height,   90
  And he held forth the child in the heartaching
    sight
Of the mother, and looked all pitiful grave, as repent-
  ing a wrong.

And there as the motherly arms stretched out with
  the thanksgiving prayer—
  And there as the mother crept up with a fearful
    swift pace,
  Till her finger nigh felt of the bairnie's face—
In a flash fierce Hamish turned round and lifted the
  child in the air,

And sprang with the child in his arms from the hor-
  rible height in the sea,
  Still screeching, "Revenge!" in the wind-rush; and
    pallid Maclean,
  Age-feeble with anger and impotent pain,
Crawled up on the crag, and lay flat, and locked hold
  of dead roots of a tree—   100

And gazed hungrily o'er, and the blood from his back
  drip-dripped in the brine,
  And a sea-hawk flung down a skeleton fish as he
    flew,
  And the mother stared white on the waste of blue,
And the wind drove a cloud to seaward, and the sun
  began to shine.
                                        —SIDNEY LANIER

THE RIME OF THE ANCIENT MARINER[1]

PART I

An ancient
Mariner meet-
eth three Gal-
lants bidden to
a wedding-
feast, and
detaineth one.

It is an ancient Mariner,
And he stoppeth one of three.
"By thy long gray beard and glittering
    eye,
Now wherefore stopp'st thou me?

"The Bridegroom's doors are opened
    wide,
And I am next of kin;
The guests are met, the feast is set:
May'st hear the merry din."

He holds him with his skinny hand,
"There was a ship," quoth he.   10
"Hold off! unhand me, gray-beard
    loon!"
Eftsoons[2] his hand dropt he.

The Wedding-
Guest is spell-
bound by the
eye of the old
seafaring man,
and constrained
to hear his tale.

He holds him with his glittering eye—
The Wedding-Guest stood still,
And listens like a three years' child:
The Mariner hath his will.

The Wedding-Guest sat on a stone:
He cannot choose but hear;
And thus spake on that ancient man,
The bright-eyed Mariner.   20

"The ship was cheered, the harbour
    cleared,
Merrily did we drop
Below the kirk,[3] below the hill,
Below the lighthouse top.

The Mariner
tells how the
ship sailed
southward with
a good wind and
fair weather, till
it reached the
line.
"The sun came up upon the left,
Out of the sea came he!
And he shone bright, and on the right
Went down into the sea.

"Higher and higher every day,
Till over the mast at noon—"   30
The Wedding-Guest here beat his
  breast,
For he heard the loud bassoon.

The Wedding-
Guest heareth
the bridal mu-
sic but the
Mariner con-
tinueth his tale.
The bride hath paced into the hall,
Red as a rose is she;
Nodding their heads before her goes
The merry minstrelsy.⁴

The Wedding-Guest he beat his breast,
Yet he cannot choose but hear;
And thus spake on that ancient man,
The bright-eyed Mariner.   40

The ship
driven by a
storm toward
the south pole.
"And now the Storm-blast came, and
  he
Was tyrannous and strong:
He struck with his o'ertaking wings,
And chased us south along.

"With sloping masts and dipping prow,
As who pursued with yell and blow
Still treads the shadow of his foe,
And forward bends his head,
The ship drove fast, loud roared the
  blast,
And southward aye we fled.   50

"And now there came both mist and
  snow.

The Rime of the Ancient Mariner   **53**

And it grew wondrous cold:
And ice, mast-high, came floating by,
As green as emerald.

The land of ice,
and of fearful
sounds where
no living thing
was to be seen.

"And through the drifts the snowy
    clifts[5]
Did send a dismal sheen:
Nor shapes of men nor beasts we
    ken—[6]
The ice was all between.

"The ice was here, the ice was there,
The ice was all around: 60
It cracked and growled, and roared and
    howled,
Like noises in a swound![7]

Till a great sea-
bird, called the
Albatross, came
through the
snow-fog, and
was received
with great joy
and hospitality.

"At length did cross an Albatross,
Through the fog it came;
As if it had been a Christian soul,
We hailed it in God's name.

"It ate the food it ne'er had eat,
And round and round it flew.
The ice did split with a thunder-fit;
The helmsman steered us through!   70

And lo! the Al-
batross proveth
a bird of good
omen, and fol-
loweth the ship
as it returned
northward
through fog and
floating ice.

"And a good south wind sprung up
    behind;
The Albatross did follow,
And every day, for food or play,
Came to the mariners' hollo!

"In mist or cloud, on mast or shroud,
It perched for vespers nine;[8]
Whiles all the night, through fog-
    smoke white
Glimmered the white moon-shine."

The ancient
Mariner in-
hospitably
killeth the
pious bird of
good omen.

"God save thee, ancient Mariner!
From the fiends, that plague thee
    thus— 80
Why look'st thou so?"—"With my
    cross-bow
I shot the Albatross.

PART II.

"The Sun now rose upon the right;
Out of the sea came he,
Still hid in mist, and on the left
Went down into the sea.

"And the good south wind still blew
    behind,
But no sweet bird did follow,
Nor any day for food or play
Came to the mariner's hollo! 90

His shipmates
cry out against
the ancient
Mariner, for
killing the
bird of good
luck.

"And I had done a hellish thing,
And it would work 'em woe:
For all averred, I had killed the bird
That made the breeze to blow.
'Ah wretch!' said they, 'the bird to slay,
That made the breeze to blow!'

But when the
fog cleared off,
they justify the
same, and thus
make them-
selves accom-
plices in the
crime.

"Nor dim nor red, like God's own head,
The glorious Sun uprist:
Then all averred, I had killed the bird
That brought the fog and mist. 100
' 'Twas right,' said they, 'such birds to
    slay,
That bring the fog and mist.

The fair breeze
continues: the
ship enters the
Pacific Ocean,
and sails north-
ward, even till
it reaches the
line.

"The fair breeze blew, the white foam
    flew,
The furrow followed free;
We were the first that ever burst
Into that silent sea.

"Down dropt the breeze, the sails dropt
    down,
'Twas sad as sad could be;
And we did speak only to break
The silence of the sea!   110

"All in a hot and copper sky,
The bloody Sun, at noon,
Right up above the mast did stand,
No bigger than the Moon.

"Day after day, day after day,
We stuck, nor breath nor motion;
As idle as a painted ship
Upon a painted ocean.

"Water, water, everywhere,   120
And all the boards did shrink;
Water, water, everywhere,
Nor any drop to drink.

"The very deep did rot: O Christ!
That ever this should be!
Yea, slimy things did crawl with legs
Upon the slimy sea.

"About, about, in reel and rout[9]
The death-fires[10] danced at night;
The water, like a witch's oils,
Burnt green, and blue, and white.   130

A spirit had
followed them;
one of the in-
visible inhabit-
ants of this
planet, neither
departed souls
nor angels;
concerning
whom the
learned Jew,
Josephus, and
the Platonic

"And some in dreams assurèd were
Of the Spirit that plagued us so;
Nine fathom deep he had followed us
From the land of mist and snow.

"And every tongue, through utter
    drought,
Was withered at the root;

Constantino-
politan,
Michael
Psellus, may
be consulted.
They are very
numerous, and
there is no cli-
mate or ele-
ment without
one or more.

We could not speak, no more than if
We had been choked with soot.

"Ah! well-a-day! what evil looks
Had I from old and young!   140
Instead of the cross, the Albatross
About my neck was hung.

PART III.

The shipmates,
in their sore
distress, would
fain throw the
whole guilt on
the ancient
Mariner: in
sign whereof
they hang the
dead sea-bird
round his neck.

"There passed a weary time. Each
        throat
Was parched, and glazed each eye.
A weary time! a weary time!
How glazed each weary eye,
When looking westward, I beheld
A something in the sky.

The ancient
Mariner be-
holdeth a sign
in the element
afar off.

"At first it seemed a little speck,
And then it seemed a mist;   150
It moved and moved, and took at last
A certain shape, I wist.[11]

"A speck, a mist, a shape, I wist!
And still it neared and neared:
As if it dodged a water-sprite,
It plunged and tacked and veered.

At its nearer
approach, it
seemeth him to
be a ship; and
at a dear ransome
he freeth
his speech from
the bonds of
thirst.

"With throats unslaked, with black
        lips baked,
We could nor laugh nor wail;
Through utter drought all dumb we
        stood!
I bit my arm, I sucked the blood,   160
And cried, 'A sail! a sail!'

"With throats unslaked, with black
        lips baked,

A flash of joy.

Agape they heard me call:
Gramercy! they for joy did grin,

And all at once their breath drew in,
As[12] they were drinking all.

And horror fol-
lows; for can it
be a ship that
comes onward
without wind
or tide?

" 'See! see!' (I cried) 'she tacks no more!
Hither to work us weal;[13]
Without a breeze, without a tide,
She steadies with upright keel!'   170

"The western wave was all a-flame,
The day was well-nigh done!
Almost upon the western wave
Rested the broad bright Sun;
When that strange shape drove
          suddenly
Bewixt us and the Sun.

It seemeth him
but the skele-
ton of a ship.

"And straight the Sun was flecked with
          bars,
(Heaven's Mother send us grace!)
As if through a dungeon-grate he
          peered
With broad and burning face.   180

" 'Alas!' (thought I, and my heart beat
          loud)
'How fast she nears and nears!
Are those her sails that glance in the
          sun,
Like restless gossameres?

And its ribs are
seen as bars on
the face of the
setting Sun.
The Spectre-
Woman and
her death-mate,
and no other
on board the
skeleton ship.
Like vessel,
like crew!

" 'Are those her ribs through which the
          sun
Did peer, as through a grate?
And is that woman all her crew?
Is that a Death? and are there two?
Is Death that woman's mate?'

"Her lips were red, her looks were free,   190

Her locks were yellow as gold:
Her skin was as white as leprosy,
The Night-mare Life-in-Death was she,
Who thicks man's blood with cold.

Death and Life-in-Death have diced for the ship's crew, and she (the latter) winneth the ancient Mariner.

"The naked hulk alongside came,
And the twain were casting dice;
'The game is done! I've won! I've won!'
Quoth she, and whistles thrice.

No twilight within the courts of the Sun.

"The Sun's rim dips; the stars rush
  out;
At one stride comes the dark;   200
With far-heard whisper, o'er the sea,
Off shot the spectre-bark.

At the rising of the Moon,

"We listened and looked sideways up!
Fear at my heart, as at a cup,
My life-blood seemed to sip!
The stars were dim, and thick the
  night,
The steersman's face by his lamp
  gleamed white
From the sails the dew did drip—
Till clomb[14] above the eastern bar
The hornèd Moon, with one bright
  star   210
Within the nether tip.

one after an-other,

"One after one, by the star-dogged
  Moon,
Too quick for groan or sigh,
Each turned his face with a ghastly
  pang,
And cursed me with his eye.

his shipmates drop down dead.

"Four times fifty living men,
(And I heard nor sigh nor groan)

With heavy thump, a lifeless lump,
They dropped down one by one.

But Life-in-
Death begins
her work on the
ancient Mar-
iner.
"The souls did from their bodies fly,— 220
They fled to bliss or woe!
And every soul, it passed me by,
Like the whizz of my cross-bow!"

PART IV.

The Wedding-
Guest feareth
that a spirit is
talking to him;
"I fear thee, ancient Mariner!
I fear thy skinny hand!
And thou art long, and lank, and
        brown,
As is the ribbed sea-sand.

but the ancient
Mariner as-
sureth him of
his bodily life,
and proceedeth
to relate his
horrible pen-
ance.
"I fear thee and thy glittering eye,
And thy skinny hand, so brown."—
"Fear not, fear not, thou Wedding-
        Guest!   230
This body dropt not down.

"Alone, alone, all, all alone,
"Alone on a wide wide sea!
And never a saint took pity on
My soul in agony.

He despiseth
the creatures of
the calm,
"The many men, so beautiful!
And they all dead did lie:
And a thousand thousand slimy things
Lived on; and so did I.

and envieth
that they should
live, and so
many lie dead.
"I looked upon the rotting sea,   240
And drew my eyes away;
I looked upon the rotting deck,
And there the dead men lay.

"I looked to heaven, and tried to pray;
But or ever a prayer had gusht,

A wicked whisper came, and made
My heart as dry as dust.

"I closed my lids, and kept them close,
And the balls like pulses beat;
For the sky and the sea, and the sea
    and the sky   250
Lay like a load on my weary eye,
And the dead were at my feet.

But the curse liveth for him in the eye of the dead men.

"The cold sweat melted from their
    limbs,
Nor rot nor reek did they:
The look with which they looked on me
Had never passed away.

In his loneliness and fixedness he yearneth towards the journeying Moon, and the stars that still sojourn, yet still move onward; and everywhere the blue sky belongs to them, and is their appointed rest, and their native country and their own natural homes, which they enter unannounced, as lords that are certainly expected and yet there is a silent joy at their arrival.

"An orphan's curse would drag to hell
A spirit from on high;
But oh! more horrible than that
Is a curse in a dead man's eye!   260
Seven days, seven nights, I saw that
    curse,
And yet I could not die.

"The moving Moon went up the sky,
And nowhere did abide:
Softly she was going up,
And a star or two beside—

"Her beams bemocked the sultry main,
Like April hoar-frost spread;
But where the ship's huge shadow lay,
The charmèd water burnt alway   270
A still and awful red.

By the light of the Moon he beholdeth God's creatures of the great calm.

"Beyond the shadow of the ship,
I watched the water-snakes:
They moved in tracks of shining white,
And when they reared, the elfish light
Fell off in hoary flakes.

"Within the shadow of the ship
I watched their rich attire:
Blue, glossy green, and velvet black,
They coiled and swam; and every
    track   280
Was a flash of golden fire.

Their beauty
and their
happiness.
He blesseth
them in his
heart.
"Oh happy living things! no tongue
Their beauty might declare:
A spring of love gushed from my heart,
And I blessed them unaware:
Sure my kind saint took pity on me,
And I blessed them unaware.

The spell begins
to break.
"The selfsame moment I could pray;
And from my neck so free
The Albatross fell off, and sank   290
Like lead into the sea.

PART V.

"Oh sleep! it is a gentle thing,
Beloved from pole to pole!
To Mary Queen the praise be given!
She sent the gentle sleep from heaven,
That slid into my soul.

By grace of the
holy Mother,
the ancient
Mariner is
refreshed with
rain.
"The silly buckets on the deck,
That had so long remained,
I dreamt that they were filled with
    dew;
And when I awoke, it rained.   300

"My lips were wet, my throat was cold,
My garments all were dank;
Sure I had drunken in my dreams,
And still my body drank.

"I moved, and could not feel my limbs

I was so light—almost
I thought that I had died in sleep,
And was a blessèd ghost.

"And soon I heard a roaring wind:
It did not come anear;   310
But with its sound it shook the sails.
That were so thin and sere.

"The upper air burst into life!
And a hundred fire-flags sheen,[15]
To and fro they were hurried about!
And to and fro, and in and out,
The wan stars danced between.

"And the coming wind did roar more
        loud,
And the sails did sigh like sedge;
And the rain poured down from one
        black cloud;   320
The Moon was at its edge.

"The thick black cloud was cleft, and
        still
The Moon was at its side:
Like waters shot from some high crag,
The lightning fell with never a jag,[16]
A river steep and wide.

"The loud wind never reached the ship,
Yet now the ship moved on!
Beneath the lightning and the Moon
The dead men gave a groan.   330

"They groaned, they stirred, they all
        uprose,
Nor spake, nor moved their eyes;
It had been strange, even in a dream,
To have seen those dead men rise.

The Rime of the Ancient Mariner   **63**

"The helmsman steered, the ship
        moved on;
Yet never a breeze up blew;
The mariners all 'gan work the ropes,
Where they were wont to do;
They raised their limbs like lifeless
        tools—
We were a ghastly crew.   340

"The body of my brother's son
Stood by me, knee to knee:
The body and I pulled at one rope,
But he said nought to me.—"

but not by the
souls of the
men, nor by
daemons of
earth or middle
air, but by a
blessed troop of
angelic spirits,
sent down by
the invocation
of the guardian
saint.

"I fear thee, ancient Mariner!"
"Be calm, thou Wedding-Guest!
'Twas not those souls that fled in pain,
Which to their corses[17] came again,
But a troop of spirits blest;

"For when it dawned—they dropped
        their arms,   350
And clustered round the mast;
Sweet sounds rose slowly through their
        mouths,
And from their bodies passed.

"Around, around, flew each sweet
        sound,
Then darted to the Sun;
Slowly the sounds came back again,
Now mixed, now one by one.

"Sometimes a-dropping from the sky
I heard the sky-lark sing;
Sometimes all little birds that are,   360
How they seemed to fill the sea and air
With their sweet jargoning![18]

"And now 'twas like all instruments,
Now like a lonely flute;
And now it is an angel's song,
That makes the heavens be mute.

"It ceased; yet still the sails made on
A pleasant noise till noon,
A noise like of a hidden brook
In the leafy month of June,   370
That to the sleeping woods all night
Singeth a quiet tune.

"Till noon we quietly sailed on,
Yet never a breeze did breathe:
Slowly and smoothly went the ship,
Moved onward from beneath.

The lonesome
Spirit from the
South pole
carries on the
ship as far as
the line, in
obedience to
the angelic
troop, but still
requireth
vengeance.

"Under the keel nine fathom deep,
From the land of mist and snow,
The spirit slid; and it was he
That made the ship to go.   380
The sails at noon left off their tune,
And the ship stood still also.

"The Sun, right up above the mast,
Had fixed her to the ocean;
But in a minute she 'gan stir,
With a short uneasy motion—
Backwards and forwards half her
        length,
With a short uneasy motion.

"Then, like a pawing horse let go,
She made a sudden bound: 390
It flung the blood into my head,
And I fell down in a swound.

"How long in that same fit I lay,
I have not to declare;[19]
But ere my living life returned,
I heard, and in my soul discerned,
Two voices in the air.

" 'Is it he?' quoth one, 'Is this the man?
By Him who died on cross,
With his cruel bow he laid full low   400
The harmless Albatross.

" 'The spirit who bideth by himself
In the land of mist and snow,
He loved the bird that loved the man
Who shot him with his bow.'

"The other was a softer voice,
As soft as honey-dew:
Quoth he, 'The man hath penance
          done,
And penance more will do.'

PART VI.

First Voice

" 'But tell me, tell me! speak again,   410
Thy soft response renewing—
What makes that ship drive on so fast?
What is the ocean doing?'

Second Voice

" 'Still as a slave before his lord,
The ocean hath no blast;
His great bright eye most silently
Up to the Moon is cast—

" 'If he may know which way to go;
For she guides him smooth or grim.
See, brother, see! how graciously   420
She looketh down on him.'

First Voice

The Mariner hath been cast into a trance; for the angelic power causeth the vessel to drive northward faster than human life could endure.

" 'But why drives on that ship so fast,
Without or wave or wind?'

Second Voice

'The air is cut away before,
And closes from behind.

" 'Fly, brother, fly, more high, more
    high!
Or we shall be belated:
For slow and slow that ship will go,
When the Mariner's trance is abated.'

The supernatural motion is retarded; the Mariner awakes, and his penance begins anew.

"I woke, and we were sailing on   430
As in a gentle weather:
'Twas night, calm night, the Moon was
    high;
The dead men stood together.

"All stood together on the deck,
For a charnel[20]-dungeon fitter:
All fixed on me their stony eyes,
That in the Moon did glitter.

"The pang, the curse, with which they
    died,
Had never passed away:
I could not draw my eyes from theirs,   440
Nor turn them up to pray.

The curse is finally expiated.

"And now this spell was snapt: once
    more
I viewed the ocean green,
And looked far forth, yet little saw
Of what had else been seen—

"Like one, that on a lonesome road

The Rime of the Ancient Mariner   **67**

Doth walk in fear and dread,
And having once turned round walks
    on,
And turns no more his head;
Because he knows, a frightful fiend   450
Doth close behind him tread.

"But soon there breathed a wind on
    me,
Nor sound nor motion made:
Its path was not upon the sea,
In ripple or in shade.

"It raised my hair, it fanned my cheek
Like a meadow-gale of spring—
It mingled strangely with my fears,
Yet it felt like a welcoming.

"Swiftly, swiftly flew the ship,   460
Yet she sailed softly too:
Sweetly, sweetly blew the breeze—
On me alone it blew.

And the ancient
Mariner
beholdeth his
native country.

"Oh! dream of joy! is this indeed
The lighthouse top I see?
Is this the hill? is this the kirk?
Is this mine own countree?

"We drifted o'er the harbour-bar,
And I with sobs did pray—
'O let me be awake, my God!   470
Or let me sleep alway.'

"The harbour-bay was clear as glass,
So smoothly it was strewn!
And on the bay the moonlight lay,
And the shadow of the Moon.

"The rock shone bright, the kirk no less,

That stands above the rock:
The moonlight steeped in silentness
The steady weathercock.

The angelic
spirits leave the
dead bodies,
and appear in
their own forms
of light.
"And the bay was white with silent
    light,   480
Till, rising from the same,
Full many shapes, that shadows were,
In crimson colours came.

"A little distance from the prow
Those crimson shadows were:
I turned my eyes upon the deck—
Oh Christ! what saw I there!

"Each corse lay flat, lifeless and flat,
And, by the holy rood! [21]
A man all light, a seraph-man,   490
On every corse there stood.

"This seraph-band, each waved his
    hand;
It was a heavenly sight!
They stood as signals to the land,
Each one a lovely light;

"This seraph-band, each waved his
    hand:
No voice did they impart—
No voice; but oh! the silence sank
Like music on my heart.

"But soon I heard the dash of oars;   500
I heard the Pilot's cheer;
My head was turned perforce away,
And I saw a boat appear.

"The Pilot and the Pilot's boy,
I heard them coming fast:

Dear Lord in Heaven! it was a joy
The dead men could not blast.

"I saw a third—I heard his voice:
It is the Hermit good!
He singeth loud his godly hymns   510
That he makes in the wood.
He'll shrieve[22] my soul, he'll wash away
The Albatross's blood.

PART VII.

The Hermit of
the wood
"This Hermit good lives in that wood
Which slopes down to the sea.
How loudly his sweet voice he rears!
He loves to talk with marineres
That come from a far countree.

"He kneels at morn, and noon, and
          eve—
He hath a cushion plump: 520
It is the moss that wholly hides
The rotted old oak-stump.

"The skiff-boat neared: I heard them
          talk,
'Why, this is strange, I trow!
Where are those lights so many and
          fair,
That signal made but now?'

approacheth
the ship with
wonder.
" 'Strange, by my faith!' the Hermit
          said—
'And they answered not our cheer!
The planks look warped! and see those
          sails,
How thin they are and sere!   530
I never saw aught like to them,
Unless perchance it were

The Rime of the Ancient Mariner   **70**

" 'Brown skeletons of leaves that lag
My forest-brook along;
When the ivy-tod[28] is heavy with snow,
And the owlet whoops to the wolf
        below,
That eats the she-wolf's young.'

" 'Dear Lord! it hath a fiendish look—'
(The Pilot made reply)
'I am a-feared'—'Push on, push on!'   540
Said the Hermit cheerily.

"The boat came closer to the ship,
But I nor spake nor stirred;
The boat came close beneath the ship,
And straight a sound was heard.

*The ship
suddenly
sinketh.*

"Under the water it rumbled on,
Still louder and more dread:
It reached the ship, it split the bay;
The ship went down like lead.

*The ancient
Mariner is
saved in the
Pilot's boat.*

"Stunned by that loud and dreadful
        sound,   550
Which sky and ocean smote,
Like one that hath been seven days
        drowned
My body lay afloat;
But, swift as dreams, myself I found
Within the Pilot's boat.

"Upon the whirl, where sank the ship,
The boat spun round and round;
And all was still, save that the hill
Was telling of the sound.

"I moved my lips—the Pilot shrieked   560
And fell down in a fit;

The holy Hermit raised his eyes,
And prayed where he did sit.

"I took the oars: the Pilot's boy,
Who now doth crazy go,
Laughed loud and long, and all the
    while
His eyes went to and fro.
'Ha! ha!' quoth he, 'full plain I see,
The Devil knows how to row.'

"And now, all in my own countree,   570
I stood on the firm land!
The Hermit stepped forth from the
    boat,
And scarcely he could stand.

" 'O shrieve me, shrieve me, holy man!'
The Hermit crossed his brow.
'Say quick,' quoth he, 'I bid thee say—
What manner of man art thou?'

"Forthwith this frame of mine was
    wrenched
With a woful agony,
Which forced me to begin my tale;   580
And then it left me free.

"Since then, at an uncertain hour,
That agony returns;
And till my ghastly tale is told,
This heart within me burns.

"I pass, like night, from land to land;
I have strange power of speech;
That moment that his face I see,
I know the man that must hear me:
To him my tale I teach.   590

"What loud uproar bursts from that
        door!
The wedding-guests are there:
But in the garden-bower the bride
And bride-maids singing are:
And hark the little vesper bell,
Which biddeth me to prayer!

"O Wedding-Guest! this soul hath been
Alone on a wide, wide sea:
So lonely 'twas, that God himself
Scarce seemèd there to be.   600

"O sweeter than the marriage-feast,
'Tis sweeter far to me,
To walk together to the kirk
With a goodly company!—

"To walk together to the kirk,
And all together pray,
While each to his great Father bends,
Old men, and babes, and loving
        friends,
And youths and maidens gay!

and to teach, by his own example, love and reverence to all things that God made and loveth.

"Farewell, farewell! but this I tell   610
To thee, thou Wedding-Guest!
He prayeth well, who loveth well
Both man and bird and beast.

"He prayeth best, who loveth best
All things both great and small;
For the dear God who loveth us,
He made and loveth all."

The Mariner, whose eye is bright,
Whose beard with age is hoar,
Is gone: and now the Wedding-Guest   620
Turned from the bridegroom's door.

He went like one that hath been
     stunned
And is of sense forlorn:[24]
A sadder and a wiser man,
He rose the morrow morn.

S. T. COLERIDGE

Here are poems of war—its glory and excitement, its waste and grief. And here are poems on the relief and release of peace.

THE DESTRUCTION OF SENNACHERIB [1]

The Assyrian came down like a wolf on the fold,
And his cohorts were gleaming in purple and gold;
And the sheen of their spears was like stars on the
    sea,
When the blue wave rolls nightly on deep Galilee.

Like the leaves of the forest when Summer is green,
That host with their banners at sunset were seen:
Like the leaves of the forest when Autumn hath
    blown,
That host on the morrow lay withered and strown.

For the Angel of Death spread his wings on the blast,
And breathed in the face of the foe as he passed;   10
And the eyes of the sleepers waxed deadly and chill,
And their hearts but once heaved, and forever grew
    still!

And there lay the steed with his nostril all wide,
But through it there rolled not the breath of his pride;
And the foam of his gasping lay white on the turf,
And cold as the spray of the rock-beating surf.

And there lay the rider distorted and pale,

With the dew on his brow, and the rust on his mail:
And the tents were all silent—the banners alone—
The lances unlifted—the trumpet unblown. 20

And the widows of Ashur[2] are loud in their wail,
And the idols are broke in the temple of Baal;[3]
And the might of the Gentile, unsmote by the sword,
Hath melted like snow in the glance of the Lord!
　　　　　　　　　—GEORGE GORDON, LORD BYRON

CAVALRY CROSSING A FORD

A line in long array where they wind betwixt green
　　islands,
They take a serpentine course, their arms flash in the
　　sun—hark to the musical clank,
Behold the silvery river, in it the splashing horses
　　loitering stop to drink,
Behold the brown-faced men, each group, each person
　　a picture, the negligent rest on the saddles,
Some emerge on the opposite bank, others are just
　　entering the ford—while,
Scarlet and blue and snowy white,
The guidon flags flutter gayly in the wind.
　　　　　　　　　—WALT WHITMAN

COME UP FROM THE FIELDS, FATHER

Come up from the fields, father, here's a letter from
　　our Pete,
And come to the front door, mother, here's a letter
　　from thy dear son.

Lo, 'tis autumn,
Lo, where the trees, deeper green, yellower and
　　redder,

Cool and sweeten Ohio's villages with leaves fluttering
in the moderate wind,
Where apples ripe in the orchards hang and grapes
on the trellised vines,
(Smell you the smell of the grapes on the vines?
Smell you the buckwheat where the bees were lately
buzzing?)

Above all, lo, the sky so calm, so transparent after the
rain, and with wondrous clouds,
Below too, all calm, all vital and beautiful, and the
farm prospers well.   10

Down in the fields all prospers well,
But now from the fields come, father, come at the
daughter's call,
And come to the entry, mother, to the front door
come right away.

Fast as she can she hurries, something ominous, her
steps trembling,
She does not tarry to smooth her hair nor adjust her
cap.

Open the envelope quickly,
O this is not our son's writing, yet his name is signed,
O a strange hand writes for our dear son, O stricken
mother's soul!
All swims before her eyes, flashes with black, she
catches the main words only,
Sentences broken, *gunshot wound in the breast,
cavalry skirmish, taken to hospital,*   20
At present low, but will soon be better.

Ah now the single figure to me,
Amid all teeming and wealthy Ohio with all its cities
and farms,

Sickly white in the face and dull in the head, very
   faint,
By the jamb of a door leans.

Grieve not so, dear mother, (the just-grown daughter
   speaks through her sobs,
The little sisters huddle around speechless and
   dismayed,)
*See, dearest mother, the letter says Pete will soon be
   better.*

Alas poor boy, he will never be better, (nor maybe
   needs to be better, that brave and simple soul,)
While they stand at home at the door he is dead
   already,
The only son is dead.

But the mother needs to be better,
She with thin form presently dressed in black,
By day her meals untouched, then at night fitfully
   sleeping, often waking,
In the midnight waking, weeping, longing with one
   deep longing,
O that she might withdraw unnoticed, silent from life
   escape and withdraw,
To follow, to seek, to be with her dear dead son.
                              —WALT WHITMAN

ARMS AND THE BOY

Let the boy try along this bayonet-blade
How cold steel is, and keen with hunger of blood;
Blue with all malice, like a madman's flash;
And thinly drawn with famishing for flesh.

Lend him to stroke these blind, blunt bullet-heads
Which long to nuzzle in the hearts of lads,
Or give him cartridges of fine zinc teeth,
Sharp with the sharpness of grief and death.

For his teeth seem for laughing round an apple.
There lurk no claws behind his fingers supple;   10
And God will grow no talons at his heels,
Nor antlers through the thickness of his curls.

—WILFRED OWEN

PEACE

Night arches England, and the winds are still;
Jasmine and honeysuckle steep the air;
Softly the stars that are all Europe's fill
Her heaven-wide dark with radiancy fair;
That shadowed moon now waxing in the west,
Stirs not a rumor in her tranquil seas;
Mysterious sleep has lulled her heart to rest,
Deep even as theirs beneath her churchyard trees.

Secure, serene; dumb now the nighthawk's threat;
The gun's low thunder drumming o'er the tide;   10
The anguish pulsing in her stricken side . . .
All is at peace. Ah, never, heart, forget
For this her youngest, best, and bravest died,
These bright dews once were mixed with blood and
      sweat.

—WALTER DE LA MARE

EVERYONE SANG

Everyone suddenly burst out singing;
And I was filled with such delight
As prisoned birds must find in freedom
Winging wildly across the white
Orchards and dark green fields; on; on;
      and out of sight.

Everyone's voice was suddenly lifted,

And beauty came like the setting sun.
My heart was shaken with tears, and horror
Drifted away. . . . O, but everyone
Was a bird; and the song was wordless; the singing
    will never be done.   10

—SIEGFRIED SASSOON

section five.

"At the Aquarium" strikes a comical note that
is echoed more seriously in "All But Blind" and
"Land of Biscay." Blindness, lack of communication,
alienation deepen into social divisiveness and
conflict in Markham's and Campbell's poems. Stephens
and Thomas write of sympathy aroused, and Humphries
of cohesiveness established. With Frost is emphasized
communication—in absence, and in presence. Fearing
deals humorously and satirically with two
modern institutions, and Francis analyzes a very
special kind of communication.

AT THE AQUARIUM

Serene the silver fishes glide,
Stern-lipped, and pale, and wonder-eyed!
As through the aged deeps of ocean,
They glide with wan and wavy motion!
They have no pathway where they go.
They flow like water to and fro.
They watch with never-winking eyes,
They watch with staring, cold surprise,
The level people in the air,
The people peering, peering there: 10
Who also wander to and fro,
And know not why or where they go,
Yet have a wonder in their eyes,
Sometimes a pale and cold surprise.

—MAX EASTMAN

ALL BUT BLIND

All but blind
  In his chambered hole
Gropes for worms
  The four-clawed Mole.

All but blind
  In the evening sky,
The hooded Bat
  Twirls softly by.

All but blind
  In the burning day   10
The Barn-Owl blunders
  On her way.

And blind as are
  These three to me,
So, blind to Someone
  I must be.

                              —WALTER DE LA MARE

THE LAND OF BISCAY

Sons of landsmen, sons of seamen, hear the tale of
      grief and me,
Looking from the land of Biscay on the waters of the
      sea.

Looking from the land of Biscay over Ocean to the
      sky
On the far-beholding foreland paced at even grief
      and I.

The Land of Biscay   82

There, as warm the west was burning and the east
uncolored cold
Down the waterway of sunset drove to shore a ship of
gold.
Gold of mast and gold of cordage, gold of sail to sight
was she,
And she glassed her ensign golden in the waters of
the sea.

Oh, said I, my friend and lover, take we now that ship
and sail
Outward in the ebb of hues and steer upon the sunset
trail;   10
Leave the night to fall behind us and the clouding
countries leave:
Help for you and me is yonder, in the havens west of
eve.

Under hill she neared the harbor, till the gazer could
behold
On the golden deck the steersman standing at the
helm of gold,
Man and ship and sky and water burning in a single
flame;
And the mariner of Ocean he was calling as he came:
From the highway of the sunset he was shouting on
the sea,
"Landsman of the land of Biscay, have you help for
grief and me?"

When I heard I did not answer, I stood mute and
shook my head:
Son of earth and son of Ocean, much we thought and
nothing said.   20
Grief and I abode the nightfall; to the sunset grief
and he
Turned them from the land of Biscay on the waters of
the sea.

—A. E. HOUSMAN

The Land of Biscay   **83**

THE MAN WITH THE HOE

Written after seeing Millet's world-famous
painting of a brutalized toiler

God created man in his own image, in the image of
God created he him.—Genesis

Bowed by the weight of centuries he leans
Upon his hoe and gazes on the ground,
The emptiness of ages in his face,
And on his back the burden of the world.
Who made him dead to rapture and despair,
A thing that grieves not and that never hopes,
Stolid and stunned, a brother to the ox?
Who loosened and let down this brutal jaw?
Whose was the hand that slanted back this brow?
Whose breath blew out the light within this brain?   10

Is this the Thing the Lord God made and gave
To have dominion over sea and land;
To trace the stars and search the heavens for power;
To feel the passion of Eternity?
Is this the dream he dreamed who shaped the suns
And marked their ways upon the ancient deep?
Down all the caverns of Hell to their last gulf
There is no shape more terrible than this—
More tongued with censure of the world's blind
    greed—
More filled with signs and portents for the soul—   20
More packt with danger to the universe.

What gulfs between him and the seraphim!
Slave of the wheel of labor, what to him
Are Plato and the swing of Pleiades?
What the long reaches of the peaks of song,
The rift of dawn, the reddening of the rose?
Through this dread shape the suffering ages look;

Time's tragedy is in that aching stoop;
Through this dread shape humanity betrayed,
Plundered, profaned and disinherited,   30
Cries protest to the powers that made the world,
A protest that is also prophecy.

O masters, lords and rulers in all lands,
Is this the handiwork you give to God,
This monstrous thing distorted and soul-quencht?
How will you ever straighten up this shape;
Touch it again with immortality;
Give back the upward looking and the light;
Rebuild in it the music and the dream;
Make right the immemorial infamies,   40
Perfidious wrongs, immedicable woes?

O masters, lords and rulers in all lands,
How will the future reckon with this Man?
How answer his brute question in that hour
When whirlwinds of rebellion shake all shores?
How will it be with kingdoms and with kings—
With those who shaped him to the thing he is—
When this dumb Terror shall rise to judge the world,
After the silence of the centuries?

                                        —EDWIN MARKHAM

THE SERF

His naked skin clothed in the torrid mist
That puffs in smoke around the patient hooves,
The ploughman drives, a slow somnambulist,
And through the green his crimson furrow grooves.
His heart, more deeply than he wounds the plain,
Long by the rasping share of insult torn,
Red clod, to which the war-cry once was rain
And tribal spears the fatal sheaves of corn,
Lies fallow now. But as the turf divides
I see in the slow progress of his strides   10

Over the toppled clods and falling flowers,
The timeless, surly patience of the serf
That ploughs the nearest to the naked earth
And ploughs down palaces, and thrones, and towers.
                                    —ROY CAMPBELL

TO THE FOUR COURTS, PLEASE

The driver rubbed at his nettly chin
With a huge, loose forefinger, crooked and black,
And his wobbly, violet lips sucked in,
And puffed out again and hung down slack:
One fang shone through his lopsided smile,
In his little pouched eye flickered years of guile.

And the horse, poor beast, it was ribbed and forked,
And its ears hung down, and its eyes were old,
And its knees were knuckly, and as we talked
It swung the stiff neck that could scarcely hold   10
Its big, skinny head up—then I stepped in,
And the driver climbed to his seat with a grin.

God help the horse and the driver too,
And the people and beasts who have never a friend,
For the driver easily might have been you,
And the horse be me by a different end.
And nobody knows how their days will cease,
And the poor, when they're old, have little of peace.
                                    —JAMES STEPHENS

THE OWL

Down hill I came, hungry, and yet not starved;
Cold, yet had heat within me that was proof
Against the North wind; tired, yet so that rest
Had seemed the sweetest thing under a roof.

Then at the inn I had food, fire, and rest,
Knowing how hungry, cold, and tired was I.
All of the night was quite barred out except
An owl's cry, a most melancholy cry

Shaken out long and clear upon the hill,
No merry note, nor cause of merriment,   10
But one telling me plain what I escaped
And others could not, that night, as in I went.

And salted was my food, and my repose,
Salted and sobered, too, by the bird's voice
Speaking for all who lay under the stars,
Soldiers and poor, unable to rejoice.
                                        —EDWARD THOMAS

NIGHT GAME

Only bores are bored,—wrote William Saroyan—
And I was a bore, and so I went to the ball game;
But there was a pest who insisted on going with me.
I thought I could shake him if I bought one ticket,
But he must have come in on a pass. I couldn't see
        him,
But I knew he was there, back of third, in the row
        behind me,
His knees in my back, and his breath coming over
        my shoulder,
The loud-mouthed fool, the sickly nervous ego,
Repeating his silly questions, like a child
Or a girl at the first game ever. *Shut up,* I told him,   10
*For Christ's sweet sake, shut up, and watch the ball
        game.*
He didn't want to, but finally subsided,
And my attention found an outward focus,
Visible, pure, objective, inning by inning,
A well-played game, with no particular features,—

Feldman pitched well, and Ott hit a couple of
   homers.

And after the ninth, with the crowd in the bleachers
   thinning,
And the lights in the grandstand dimming out behind
   us,
And a full moon hung before us, over the clubhouse,
I drifted out with the crowd across the diamond,   20
Over the infield brown and the smooth green outfield,
So wonderful underfoot, so right, so perfect,
That each of us was a player for a moment,
The men my age, and the soldiers and the sailors,
Their girls, and the running kids, and the plodding
   old men,
Taking it easy, the same unhurried tempo,
In the mellow light and air, in the mild cool weather,
Moving together, moving out together,
Oh, this is good, I felt, to be part of this movement,
This mood, this music, part of the human race,   30
Alike and different, after the game is over,
Streaming away to the exit, and underground.

                     —ROLFE HUMPHRIES

THE WOOD-PILE

Out walking in the frozen swamp one grey day,
I paused and said, "I will turn back from here.
No, I will go on farther—and we shall see."
The hard snow held me, save where now and then
One foot went through. The view was all in lines
Straight up and down of tall slim trees
Too much alike to mark or name a place by
So as to say for certain I was here
Or somewhere else: I was just far from home.
A small bird flew before me. He was careful   10
To put a tree between us when he lighted,
And say no word to tell me who he was

Who was so foolish as to think what *he* thought.
He thought that I was after him for a feather—
The white one in his tail; like one who takes
Everything said as personal to himself.
One flight out sideways would have undeceived him.
And then there was a pile of wood for which
I forgot him and let his little fear
Carry him off the way I might have gone,   20
Without so much as wishing him good-night.
He went behind it to make his last stand.
It was a cord of maple, cut and split
And piled—and measured, four by four by eight.
And not another like it could I see.
No runner tracks in this year's snow looped near it.
And it was older sure than this year's cutting,
Or even last year's or the year's before.
The wood was grey and the bark warping off it
And the pile somewhat sunken. Clematis   30
Had wound strings round and round it like a bundle.
What held it though on one side was a tree
Still growing, and on one a stake and prop,
These latter about to fall. I thought that only
Someone who lived in turning to fresh tasks
Could so forget his handiwork on which
He spent himself, the labor of his axe,
And leave it there far from a useful fireplace
To warm the frozen swamp as best it could
With the slow smokeless burning of decay.   40

—ROBERT FROST

THE AXE-HELVE

I've known ere now an interfering branch
Of alder catch my lifted axe behind me.
But that was in the woods, to hold my hand
From striking at another alder's roots,
And that was, as I say, an alder branch.
This was a man, Baptiste, who stole one day

Behind me on the snow in my own yard
Where I was working at the chopping-block,
And cutting nothing not cut down already.
He caught my axe expertly on the rise,   10
When all my strength put forth was in his favor,
Held it a moment where it was, to calm me,
Then took it from me—and I let him take it.
I didn't know him well enough to know
What it was all about. There might be something
He had in mind to say to a bad neighbor
He might prefer to say to him disarmed.
But all he had to tell me in French-English
Was what he thought of—not me, but my axe;
Me only as I took my axe to heart.   20
It was the bad axe-helve someone had sold me—
"Made on machine," he said, ploughing the grain
With a thick thumbnail to show how it ran
Across the handle's long drawn serpentine,
Like the two strokes across a dollar sign.
"You give her one good crack, she's snap raght off.
Den where's your hax-ead flying t'rough de hair?"
Admitted; and yet, what was that to him?

"Come on my house and I put you one in
What's las' awhile—good hick'ry what's grow crooked,   30
De second growt' I cut myself—tough, tough!"

Something to sell? That wasn't how it sounded.

"Den when you say you come? It's cost you nothing.
To-naght?"

               As well tonight as any night.

Beyond an over-warmth of kitchen stove
My welcome differed from no other welcome.
Baptiste knew best why I was where I was.
So long as he would leave enough unsaid,
I shouldn't mind his being overjoyed

(If overjoyed he was) at having got me   40
Where I must judge if what he knew about an axe
That not everybody else knew was to count
For nothing in the measure of a neighbor.
Hard if, though cast away for life with Yankees,
A Frenchman couldn't get his human rating!

Mrs. Baptiste came in and rocked a chair
That had as many motions as the world:
One back and forward, in and out of shadow,
That got her nowhere; one more gradual,
Sideways, that would have run her on the stove   50
In time, had she not realized her danger
And caught herself up bodily, chair and all,
And set herself back where she started from.
"She ain't spick too much Henglish—dat's too bad."

I was afraid, in brightening first on me,
Then on Baptiste, as if she understood
What passed between us, she was only feigning.
Baptiste was anxious for her; but no more
Than for himself, so placed he couldn't hope
To keep his bargain of the morning with me   60
In time to keep me from suspecting him
Of really never having meant to keep it.

Needlessly soon he had his axe-helves out,
A quiverful to choose from, since he wished me
To have the best he had, or had to spare—
Not for me to ask which, when what he took
Had beauties he had to point me out at length
To insure their not being wasted on me.
He liked to have it slender as a whipstock,
Free from the least knot, equal to the strain   70
Of bending like a sword across the knee.
He showed me that the lines of a good helve
Were native to the grain before the knife
Expressed them, and its curves were no false curves
Put on it from without. And there its strength lay

For the hard work. He chafed its long white body
From end to end with his rough hand shut round it.
He tried it at the eye-hole in the axe-head.
"Hahn, hahn," he mused, "don't need much taking
    down."
Baptiste knew how to make a short job long   80
For love of it, and yet not waste time either.

Do you know, what we talked about was knowledge?
Baptiste on his defence about the children
He kept from school, or did his best to keep—
Whatever school and children and our doubts
Of laid-on education had to do
With the curves of his axe-helves and his having
Used these unscrupulously to bring me
To see for once the inside of his house.
Was I desired in friendship, partly as someone   90
To leave it to, whether the right to hold
Such doubts of education should depend
Upon the education of those who held them?

But now he brushed the shavings from his knee
And stood the axe there on its horse's hoof,
Erect, but not without its waves, as when
The snake stood up for evil in the Garden,—
Top-heavy with a heaviness his short,
Thick hand made light of, steel-blue chin drawn
    down
And in a little—a French touch in that.   100
Baptiste drew back and squinted at it, pleased;
"See how she's cock her head!"

                            —ROBERT FROST

KING JUKE

The jukebox has a big square face,
A majestic face, softly glowing with red and green
    and purple lights.

Have you got a face as bright as that?

BUT IT'S A PROVEN FACT, THAT A JUKEBOX HAS
    NO EARS.

With its throat of brass, the jukebox eats live nickels
    raw;
It can turn itself on or shut itself off;
It has no hangovers, knows no regrets, and it never
    feels the need for sleep.
Can you do that?
What can you do that a jukebox can't, and do it ten
    times better than you?

And it hammers at your nerves, and stabs you
    through the heart, and beats upon your soul—   10
But can you do that to the box?

Its resourceful mind, filled with thoughts that range
    from love to grief, from the gutter to the stars,
    from pole to pole,
Can seize its thoughts between fingers of steel,
Begin them at the start and follow them through in
    an orderly fashion to the very end.
Can you do that?
And what can you say that a jukebox can't, and say
    it in a clearer, louder voice than yours?
What have you got, a jukebox hasn't got?

Well, a jukebox has no ears, they say.
The box, it is believed, cannot even hear itself.
IT SIMPLY HAS NO EARS AT ALL.   20
                    —KENNETH FEARING

TRAVELOGUE IN A SHOOTING-GALLERY

There is a jungle, there is a jungle, there is a vast,

wild, wild, marvelous, marvelous, marvelous
jungle,
Open to the public during business hours,
A jungle not very far from an Automat, between a hat
store there, and a radio shop.

There, there, whether it rains, or it snows, or it
shines,
Under the hot, blazing, cloudless, tropical neon skies
that the management always arranges there,
Rows and rows of marching ducks, dozens and
dozens and dozens of ducks, move steadily along
on smoothly-oiled ballbearing feet,
Ducks as big as telephone books, slow and fearless
and out of this world,
While lines and lines of lions, lions, rabbits, pan-
thers, elephants, crocodiles, zebras, apes,
Filled with jungle hunger and jungle rage and jungle
love,
Stalk their prey on endless, endless rotary belts   10
through never-ending forests, and burning des-
erts, and limitless veldts,
To the sound of tom-toms, equipped with silencers,
beaten by thousands of savages hidden there.

And there it is that all the big-game hunters go, there
the traders and the explorers come,
Lean-faced men with windswept eyes who arrive by
streetcar, auto or subway, taxi or on foot, street-
car or bus,
And they nod, and they say, and they need no more:
"There . . . there . . .
There they come and there they go."
And weighing machines, in this civilized jungle, will
read your soul like an open book, for a penny
at a time, and tell you all,
There, there, where smoking is permitted,
In a jungle that lies, like a rainbow's end, at the very
end of every trail,

Travelogue in a Shooting-Gallery   **94**

There, in the only jungle in the whole wide world
   where ducks are waiting for streetcars,
And hunters can be psychoanalyzed, while they
   smoke and wait for ducks.   20

—KENNETH FEARING

PITCHER

His art is eccentricity, his aim
How not to hit the mark he seems to aim at,

His passion how to avoid the obvious,
His technique how to vary the avoidance.

The others throw to be comprehended. He
Throws to be a moment misunderstood.

Yet not too much. Not errant, arrant, wild,
But every seeming aberration willed.

Not to, yet still, still to communicate
Making the batter understand too late.

—ROBERT FRANCIS

Here the poet is in love and,
"ah woe betide," out of love.

WHEN, IN DISGRACE
WITH FORTUNE AND MEN'S EYES

When, in disgrace with fortune and men's eyes,
I all alone beweep my outcast state,
And trouble deaf heaven with my bootless[1] cries,
And look upon myself, and curse my fate,
Wishing me like to one more rich in hope,
Featured like him, like him with friends possessed,
Desiring this man's art, and that man's scope,
With what I most enjoy contented least;
Yet in these thoughts myself almost despising,
Haply I think on thee, and then my state,   10
Like to the lark at break of day arising
From sullen earth, sings hymns at heaven's gate;
  For thy sweet love remembered such wealth
   brings
  That then I scorn to change my state with kings.
       —WILLIAM SHAKESPEARE

SHE WALKS IN BEAUTY

She walks in beauty, like the night
 Of cloudless climes and starry skies;
And all that's best of dark and bright
 Meet in her aspect and her eyes:
Thus mellowed to that tender light
 Which heaven to gaudy day denies.

One shade the more, one ray the less,
  Had half impaired the nameless grace
Which waves in every raven tress,
  Or softly lightens o'er her face;   10
Where thoughts serenely sweet express
  How pure, how dear their dwelling-place.

And on that cheek, and o'er that brow,
  So soft, so calm, yet eloquent,
The smiles that win, the tints that glow,
  But tell of days in goodness spent,
A mind at peace with all below,
  A heart whose love is innocent!
                          —GEORGE GORDON, LORD BYRON

MAID OF ATHENS, ERE WE PART
Ζωή μου, σᾶς ἀγαπῶ.

Maid of Athens, ere we part,
Give, oh, give me back my heart!
Or, since that has left my breast,
Keep it now, and take the rest!
Hear my vow before I go,
Ζωή μου, σᾶς ἀγαπῶ.[1]

By those tresses unconfined,
Wooed by each Aegean wind;
By those lids whose jetty fringe
Kiss thy soft cheeks' blooming tinge;   10
By those wild eyes like the roe,
Ζωή μου, σᾶς ἀγαπῶ.

By that lip I long to taste;
By that zone-encircled waist;
By all the token-flowers that tell
What words can never speak so well;
By love's alternate joy and woe,
Ζωή μου, σᾶς ἀγαπῶ.

Maid of Athens! I am gone:
Think of me, sweet! when alone.
Though I fly to Istanbul,
Athens holds my heart and soul:
Can I cease to love thee? No!
Ζωή μου, σᾶς ἀγαπῶ.

—GEORGE GORDON, LORD BYRON

20

MEETING AT NIGHT

The gray sea and the long black land;
And the yellow half-moon large and low;
And the startled little waves that leap
In fiery ringlets from their sleep,
As I gain the cove with pushing prow,
And quench its speed in the slushy sand.

Then a mile of warm sea-scented beach;
Three fields to cross till a farm appears;
A tap at the pane, the quick sharp scratch
And blue spurt of a lighted match,
And a voice less loud, through its joys and fears,
Than the two hearts beating each to each!

10

PARTING AT MORNING

Round the cape of a sudden came the sea,
And the sun looked over the mountain's rim:
And straight was a path of gold for him,
And the need of a world of men for me.

—ROBERT BROWNING

LA BELLE DAME SANS MERCI

Ah, what can ail thee, knight-at-arms
   Alone and palely loitering;

The sedge[1] is wither'd from the lake,
   And no birds sing.

Ah, what can ail thee, knight-at-arms,
   So haggard and so woe-begone?
The squirrel's granary is full,
   And the harvest's done.

I see a lily on thy brow,
   With anguish moist and fever dew;   10
And on thy cheek a fading rose
   Fast withereth too.

I met a lady in the meads[2]
   Full beautiful, a faery's child;
Her hair was long, her foot was light,
   And her eyes were wild.

I set her on my pacing steed,
   And nothing else saw all day long;
For sideways would she lean, and sing
   A faery's song.   20

I made a garland for her head,
   And bracelets too, and fragrant zone;[3]
She look'd at me as she did love,
   And made sweet moan.

She found me roots of relish sweet,
   And honey wild, and manna dew;
And sure in language strange she said,
   I love thee true.

She took me to her elfin grot,[4]
   And there she wept and sigh'd full sore,   30
And there I shut her wild, wild eyes
   With kisses four.

And there she lulled me asleep,
   And there I dream'd, ah woe betide,

La Belle Dame Sans Merci   **99**

The latest dream I ever dream'd
On the cold hill side.

I saw pale kings, and princes too,
Pale warriors, death-pale were they all;
Who cry'd—"La belle Dame sans merci
Hath thee in thrall!" [5]   40

I saw their starv'd lips in the gloam
With horrid warning gaped wide,
And I awoke, and found me here
On the cold hill side.

And this is why I sojourn here
Alone and palely loitering,
Though the sedge is wither'd from the lake,
And no birds sing.

—JOHN KEATS

section seven.

Walt Whitman's praise of animals (and dispraise
of their "superiors") leads off a series of poems
that are concerned with the lower creatures and
man's relationship with them. The excerpt on page 102
from one of John Muir's books, the only prose passage
in the anthology, may provide a fruitful contrast
with the poem that follows it.

ANIMALS
(From *Song of Myself*)

I think I could turn and live with animals, they are
     so placid and self-contained;
I stand and look at them long and long.
They do not sweat and whine about their condition;
They do not lie awake in the dark and weep for their
     sins;
They do not make me sick discussing their duty to
     God;
Not one is dissatisfied—not one is demented with the
     mania of owning things;
Not one kneels to another, nor to his kind that lived
     thousands of years ago;
Not one is respectable or industrious over the whole
     earth.

               —WALT WHITMAN

THE WATER OUZEL
From *The Mountains of California*

The waterfalls of the Sierra are frequented by only one bird,—the Ouzel or Water Thrush *(Cinclus mexicanus, Sw.).* He is a singularly joyous and lovable little fellow, about the size of a robin, clad in a plain waterproof suit of bluish gray, with a tinge of chocolate on the head and shoulders. In form he is about as smoothly plump and compact as a pebble that has been whirled in a pot-hole, the flowing contour of his body being interrupted only by his strong feet and bill, the crisp wing-tips, and the upslanted wren-like tail.

Among all the countless waterfalls I have met in the course of ten years' exploration in the Sierra, whether among the icy peaks, or warm foot-hills, or in the profound yosemitic cañons of the middle region, not one was found without its Ouzel. No cañon is too cold for this little bird, none too lonely, provided it be rich in falling water. Find a fall, or cascade, or rushing rapid, anywhere upon a clear stream, and there you will surely find its complementary Ouzel, flitting about in the spray, diving in foaming eddies, whirling like a leaf among beaten foam-balls; ever vigorous and enthusiastic, yet self-contained, and neither seeking nor shunning your company.

If disturbed while dipping about in the margin shallows, he either sets off with a rapid whir to some other feeding-ground up or down the stream, or alights on some half-submerged rock or snag out in the current, and immediately begins to nod and curtsy like a wren, turning his head from side to side with many other odd dainty movements that never fail to fix the attention of the observer.

He is the mountain streams' own darling, the humming-bird of blooming waters, loving rocky ripple-slopes and sheets of foam as a bee loves flowers, as a lark loves sunshine and meadows. Among all the mountain birds, none has cheered me so much in my lonely wanderings,— none so unfailingly. For both in winter and summer he sings, sweetly, cheerily, independent alike of sunshine and of love, requiring no other inspiration than the stream on which he dwells. While water sings, so must he, in heat or cold, calm or storm, ever attuning his voice in sure accord; low in the drought of summer and the drought of winter, but never silent.

During the golden days of Indian summer, after most of the snow has been melted, and the mountain streams have become feeble,—a succession of silent pools, linked together by shallow, transparent currents and strips of silvery lacework—then the song of the Ouzel is at its lowest ebb. But as soon as the winter clouds have bloomed, and the mountain treasuries are once more replenished with snow, the voices of the streams and ouzels increase in strength and richness until the flood season of early summer. Then the torrents chant their noblest anthems, and then is the flood-time of our songster's melody. As for weather, dark days and sun days are the same to him. The voices of most song-birds, however joyous, suffer a long winter eclipse; but the Ouzel sings on through all the seasons and every kind of storm. Indeed no storm can be more violent than those of the waterfalls in the midst of which he delights to dwell. However dark and boisterous the weather, snowing, blowing, or cloudy, all the same he sings, and with never a note of sadness. No need of spring sunshine to thaw *his* song, for it never freezes. Never shall you hear anything wintry from *his* warm breast; no pinched cheeping, no wavering notes between sorrow and joy; his mellow, fluty voice is ever tuned to downright gladness, as free from dejection as cock-crowing.

It is pitiful to see wee frost-pinched sparrows on cold mornings in the mountain groves shaking the snow from their feathers, and hopping about as if anxious to be cheery, then hastening back to their hidings out of the wind, puffing out their breast-feathers over their toes, and subsiding among the leaves, cold and breakfastless, while the snow continues to fall, and there is no sign of clearing. But the Ouzel never calls forth a single touch of pity; not because he is strong to endure, but rather because he seems to live a charmed life beyond the reach of every influence that makes endurance necessary.

. . . .

What may be regarded as the separate songs of the Ouzel are exceedingly difficult of description, because they are so variable and at the same time so confluent. Though I have been acquainted with my favorite ten years, and during most of this time have heard him sing nearly every day, I still detect notes and strains that seem new to me. Nearly all of his music is sweet and tender, lapsing from his round breast like water over the smooth lip of a pool, then breaking farther on into a sparkling foam of melodious notes, which glow with subdued enthusiasm, yet without expressing much of the strong, gushing ecstasy of the bobolink or skylark.

The more striking strains are perfect arabesques of melody, composed of a few full, round, mellow notes, embroidered with delicate trills which fade and melt in long slender cadences. In a general way his music is that of the streams refined and spiritualized. The deep booming notes of the falls are in it, the trills of rapids, the gurgling of margin eddies, the low whispering of level reaches, and the sweet tinkle' of separate drops oozing from the ends of mosses and falling into tranquil pools.

The Ouzel never sings in chorus with other birds, nor with his kind, but only with the streams. And like flowers that bloom beneath the surface of the ground, some of our favorite's best song-blossoms never rise above the surface of the heavier music of the water. I have often observed him singing in the midst of beaten spray, his music completely buried beneath the water's roar; yet I knew he was surely singing by his gestures and the movements of his bill.

The Water Ouzel   104

His food, as far as I have noticed, consists of all kinds of water insects, which in summer are chiefly procured along shallow margins. Here he wades about ducking his head under water and deftly turning over pebbles and fallen leaves with his bill, seldom choosing to go into deep water where he has to use his wings in diving.

He seems to be especially fond of the larvae of mosquitos, found in abundance attached to the bottom of smooth rock channels where the current is shallow. When feeding in such places he wades upstream, and often while his head is under water the swift current is deflected upward along the glossy curves of his neck and shoulders, in the form of a clear, crystalline shell, which fairly incloses him like a bell-glass, the shell being broken and re-formed as he lifts and dips his head; while ever and anon he sidles out to where the too powerful current carries him off his feet; then he dexterously rises on the wing and goes gleaning again in shallower places.

But during the winter, when the stream-banks are embossed in snow, and the streams themselves are chilled nearly to the freezing-point, so that the snow falling into them in stormy weather is not wholly dissolved, but forms a thin, blue sludge, thus rendering the current opaque— then he seeks the deeper portions of the main rivers, where he may dive to clear water beneath the sludge. Or he repairs to some open lake or millpond, at the bottom of which he feeds in safety. . . .

The Ouzel seldom swims more than a few yards on the surface, for, not being web-footed, he makes rather slow progress, but by means of his strong, crisp wings he swims, or rather flies, with celerity under the surface, often to considerable distances. But it is in withstanding the force of heavy rapids that his strength of wing in this respect is most strikingly manifested. The following may be regarded as a fair illustration of his power of sub-aquatic flight. One stormy morning in winter when the Merced River was blue and green with unmelted snow, I observed one of my Ouzels perched on a snag out in the midst of a swift-rushing rapid, singing cheerily, as if everything was just to his mind; and while I stood on the bank admiring him, he suddenly plunged into the sludgy current, leaving his song abruptly broken off. After feeding a minute or two at the bottom, and when one would suppose that he must inevitably be swept far down-stream, he emerged just where he went down, alighted on the same snag, showered the water-beads from his feathers, and continued his unfinished song, seemingly in tranquil ease as if it had suffered no interruption.

The Ouzel alone of all birds dares to enter a white torrent. And though strictly terrestrial in structure, no other is so inseparably related to water, not even the duck or the bold ocean albatross, or the stormy-petrel. For ducks go ashore as soon as they finish feeding in undisturbed places, and very often make long flights overland from lake to lake or field to field. The same is true of most other aquatic birds. But the Ouzel, born on the brink of a stream, or on a snag or boulder in the midst of it, seldom leaves it for a single moment. For, notwithstanding he is often on the wing, he never flies overland, but whirs with rapid, quail-like beat above the stream, tracing all its windings. Even when the stream is quite small, say from five to ten feet wide, he seldom shortens his flight by crossing a bend, however abrupt it may be; and even when disturbed by meeting some one on the bank, he prefers to fly over one's head, to dodging out over the ground. When, therefore, his flight along a crooked stream is viewed endwise, it appears most strikingly wavered— a description on the air of every curve with lightning-like rapidity.

The vertical curves and angles of the most precipitous torrents he traces with the same rigid fidelity, swooping down the inclines of cascades, dropping sheer over dizzy falls amid the spray, and ascending with the same fearlessness and ease, seldom seeking to lessen the steepness of the aclivity by beginning to ascend before reaching the base of the fall. No matter though it may be several hundred feet in height he holds straight on, as if about to dash headlong into the throng of booming rockets, then darts abruptly upward, and, after alighting at the top of the precipice to rest a moment, proceeds to feed and sing. His flight is solid and impetuous, without any intermission of wing-beats,—one homogeneous buzz like that of a laden bee on its way home. And while thus buzzing freely from fall to fall, he is frequently heard giving utterance to a long outdrawn train of unmodulated notes, in no way connected with his song, but corresponding closely with his flight in sustained vigor.

. . . .

Such, then, is our little Cinclus, beloved of every one who is so fortunate as to know him. Tracing on strong wing every curve of the most precipitous torrents from one extremity of the Sierra to the other; not fearing to follow them through their darkest gorges and coldest snow-tunnels; acquainted with every waterfall, echoing their divine music; and throughout the whole of their beautiful lives interpreting all that we in our unbelief call terrible in the utterances of torrents and storms, as only varied expressions of God's eternal love.

—JOHN MUIR

WATER OUZEL

To Dora Wilson

Follow back from the gull's bright arc and the
    osprey's plunge,
Past the silent heron, erect in the tidal marsh,
Up the mighty river, rolling in mud. Branch off
At the sign of the kingfisher poised on a twisted snag.
Not deceived when the surface grows calm, keep on,
Past the placidity of ducks, the delusive pastoral
    dreams
Drawn down by the effortless swallows that drink on
    the wing.
With the wheat fields behind you, do not neglect to
    choose
At every juncture the clearest and coldest path.

Push through the reeds where the redwing sways, 10
Climb through the warnings of hidden jays,
Climb, climb the jostling, narrowing stream
Through aspen sunlight into the evergreen darkness
Where chattering crossbills scatter the shreds of
cones.
Here at last at the brink of the furthest fall,
With the water dissolving to mist as it shatters the
pool below,
Pause beneath timber-line springs and the melting
snow.
Here, where the shadows are deep in the crystal air,
So near a myriad beginnings, after so long a journey,
Expecting at least a golden cockatoo 20
Or a screaming eagle with wings of flame,
Stifle your disappointment, observe
The burgher of all this beauty, the drab
Citizen of the headwaters; struggle to love
The ridiculous ouzel, perched on his slippery stone
Like an awkward, overblown catbird deprived of its
tail.
Not for him the limitless soaring above the storm,
Or the surface-skimming, or swimming, or plunging
in.
He walks. In the midst of the turbulence, bathed in
spray,
From a rock without foothold into the lunging current 30
He descends a deliberate step at a time till, sub-
merged,
He has walked from sight and hope. The stream
Drives on, dashes, splashes, drops over the edge,
Too swift for ice in midwinter, too cold
For life in midsummer, depositing any debris,
Leaf, twig or carcass, along the way,
Wedging them in behind rocks to rot,
Such as these not reaching the ocean.

Yet, lo, the lost one emerges unharmed,
Hardly wet as he walks from the water. 40

Water Ouzel   **108**

Undisturbed by beauty or terror, pursuing
His own few needs with a nerveless will,
Nonchalant in the torrent, he bobs and nods
As though to acknowledge implicit applause.
This ceaseless tic, a trick of the muscles shared
With the solitary sandpiper, burlesqued
By the teeter-bob and the phoebe's tail,
Is not related to approbation. The dipper,
Denied the adventure of uncharted flight
Over vast waters to an unknown homeland, denied   50
Bodily beauty, slightly absurd and eccentric,
Will never attain acclaim as a popular hero.
No prize committee selects the clown
Whose only dangers are daily and domestic.

Yet he persists, and does not consider it persisting.
On a starless, sub-zero, northern night,
When all else has taken flight into sleep or the south,
He, on the edge of the stream, has been heard to
    repeat
The rippling notes of his song, which are clear and
    sweet.

                                    —WILLIAM H. MATCHETT

ALL THE LITTLE HOOFPRINTS

Farther up the gorge the sea's voice fainted and
    ceased.
We heard a new noise far away ahead of us, vague
    and metallic, it might have been some un-
    pleasant bird's voice
Bedded in a matrix of long silences. At length we
    came to a little cabin lost in the redwoods,
An old man sat on a bench before the doorway filing
    a cross-cut saw; sometimes he slept,
Sometimes he filed. Two or three horses in the corral
    by the streamside lifted their heads
To watch us pass, but the old man did not.

In the afternoon we
returned the same way,
And had the picture in our minds of magnificent
regions of space and mountain not seen before.
(This was
The first time that we visited Pigeon Gap, whence
you look down behind the great shouldering
pyramid-
Edges of Pico Blanco through eagle-gulfs of air to a
forest basin
Where two-hundred-foot redwoods look like the pile   10
on a Turkish carpet.) With such extension of
the idol-
Worshipping mind we came down the streamside.
The old man was still at his post by the cabin
doorway, but now
Stood up and stared, said angrily, "Where are you
camping?" I said, "We're not camping, we're
going home." He said
From his flushed heavy face, "That's the way fires get
started. Did you come at night?" "We passed
you this morning.
You were half asleep, filing a saw." "I'll kill anybody
that starts a fire here . . ." his voice quavered
Into bewilderment . . . "I didn't see you. Kind of
feeble I guess.
My temperature's a hundred and two every afternoon." "Why, what's the matter?" He removed
his hat
And rather proudly showed us a deep healed trench
in the bald skull. "My horse fell at the ford,
I must 'a' cracked my head on a rock. Well, sir, I
can't remember anything till next morning.
I woke in bed the pillow was soaked with blood the
horse was in the corral and had had his hay,"—   20
Singing the words as if he had told the story a hundred times. To whom? To himself, probably,—
"The saddle was on the rack and the bridle on the

All the Little Hoofprints   **110**

right nail. What do you think of *that* now?" He passed

His hand on his bewildered forehead and said, "Unless an angel or something came down and did it.

A basin of blood and water by the crick, I must 'a' washed myself." My wife said sharply, "Have you been to a doctor?"

"Oh yes," he said, "my boy happened down." She said, "You oughtn't to be alone here: are you all alone here?"

"No," he answered, "horses. I've been all over the world: right here is the most beautiful place in the world.

I played the piccolo in ships' orchestras." We looked at the immense redwoods and dark

Fern-taken slip of land by the creek, where the horses were, and the yuccaed hillsides high in the sun

Flaring like torches; I said, "Darkness comes early here." He answered with pride and joy, "Two hundred and eighty-

Five days in the year the sun never gets in here. 30

Like living under the sea, green all summer, beautiful." My wife said, "How do you know your temperature's

A hundred and two?" "Eh? The doctor. He said the bone

Presses my brain, he's got to cut out a piece. I said 'All right, you've got to wait till it rains,

I've got to guard my place through the fire-season.' By God," he said joyously,

"The quail on my roof wake me up every morning, then I look out the window and a dozen deer

Drift up the canyon with the mist on their shoulders. Look in the dust at your feet, all the little hoofprints."

—ROBINSON JEFFERS

All the Little Hoofprints   111

SNAKE

A snake came to my water-trough
On a hot, hot day, and I in pyjamas for the heat,
To drink there.

In the deep, strange-scented shade of the great dark
    carob-tree
I came down the steps with my pitcher
And must wait, must stand and wait, for there he was
    at the trough before me.

He reached down from a fissure in the earth-wall in
    the gloom
And trailed his yellow-brown slackness soft-bellied
    down, over the edge of the stone trough,
And rested his throat upon the stone bottom,   10
And where the water had dripped from the tap, in
    a small clearness,
He sipped with his straight mouth,
Softly drank through his straight gums, into his slack
    long body,
Silently.

Someone was before me at my water-trough,
And I, like a second comer, waiting.

He lifted his head from his drinking, as cattle do,
And looked at me vaguely, as drinking cattle do,
And flickered his two-forked tongue from his lips,
    and mused a moment,
                                     20
And stooped and drank a little more,

Being earth-brown, earth-golden from the burning
    bowels of the earth
On the day of Sicilian July, with Etna smoking.

The voice of my education said to me
He must be killed,
For in Sicily the black, black snakes are innocent,
    the gold are venomous.

And voices in me said, If you were a man
You would take a stick and break him now, and finish
    him off.

But must I confess how I liked him,
How glad I was he had come like a guest in quiet, to
    drink at my water-trough
And depart peaceful, pacified, and thankless,   30
Into the burning bowels of this earth?

Was it cowardice, that I dared not kill him?
Was it perversity, that I longed to talk to him?
Was it humility, to feel so honoured?
I felt so honoured.

And yet those voices:
If you were not afraid, you would kill him!

And truly I was afraid, I was most afraid,
But even so, honoured still more
That he should seek my hospitality   40
From out the dark door of the secret earth.

He drank enough
And lifted his head, dreamily, as one who has
    drunken,
And flickered his tongue like a forked night on the
    air, so black,
Seeming to lick his lips,
And looked around like a god, unseeing, into the air,
And slowly turned his head,
And slowly, very slowly, as if thrice adream,
Proceeded to draw his slow length curving round
And climb again the broken bank of my wall-face.   50

Snake   **113**

And as he put his head into that dreadful hole,
And as he slowly drew up, snake-easing his shoulders,
    and entered farther,
A sort of horror, a sort of protest against his with-
    drawing into that horrid black hole,
Deliberately going into the blackness, and slowly
    drawing himself after,
Overcame me now his back was turned.

I looked round, I put down my pitcher,
I picked up a clumsy log
And threw it at the water-trough with a clatter.

I think it did not hit him,
But suddenly that part of him that was left behind
    convulsed in undignified haste,   60
Writhed like lightning, and was gone
Into the black hole, the earth-lipped fissure in the wall-
    front,
At which, in the intense still noon, I stared with
    fascination.

And immediately I regretted it.
I thought how paltry, how vulgar, what a mean act!
I despised myself and the voices of my accursed
    human education.

And I thought of the albatross,
And I wished he would come back, my snake.

For he seemed to me again like a king,
Like a king in exile, uncrowned in the underworld,   70
Now due to be crowned again.

And so, I missed my chance with one of the lords
Of life.
And I have something to expiate:
A pettiness.

                —D. H. LAWRENCE

HURT HAWKS

I.

The broken pillar of the wing jags from the clotted
    shoulder,
The wing trails like a banner in defeat,
No more to use the sky forever but live with famine
And pain a few days: cat nor coyote
Will shorten the week of waiting for death, there is
    game without talons.
He stands under the oak-bush and waits
The lame feet of salvation; at night he remembers
    freedom
And flies in a dream, the dawns ruin it.
He is strong and pain is worse to the strong, in-
    capacity is worse.
The curs of the day come and torment him   10
At distance, no one but death the redeemer will
    humble that head,
The intrepid readiness, the terrible eyes.
The wild God of the world is sometimes merciful to
    those
That ask mercy, not often to the arrogant.
You do not know him, you communal people, or you
    have forgotten him;
Intemperate and savage, the hawk remembers him;
Beautiful and wild, the hawks, and men that are
    dying, remember him.

II.

I'd sooner, except the penalties, kill a man than a
    hawk; but the great redtail
Had nothing left but unable misery
From the bone too shattered for mending, the wing
    that trailed under his talons when he moved.   20
We had fed him six weeks, I gave him freedom,

He wandered over the foreland hill and returned in
    the evening, asking for death,
Not like a beggar, still eyed with the old
Implacable arrogance. I gave him the lead gift in the
    twilight.
                          What fell was relaxed,
Owl-downy, soft feminine feathers; but what
Soared: the fierce rush; the night-herons by the
    flooded river cried fear at its rising
Before it was quite unsheathed from reality.
                              —ROBINSON JEFFERS

THE LIVES OF GULLS AND CHILDREN

Around the headland, at the end
Where they had not been before,
Paced by the white and the grey gull
With loud shrieking, and by the neat
Black-hooded tern, they found the place of death.
When they looked back along their way they saw
The footprints lonely and loud on the sand.

Few bones at first their feet kicked up,
Then more a flat thicket of bone
And tangled cartilage, dry white and clean,   10
Tasting of salt when the children licked them.
Further on were feathers, then flesh
Strung on the bone ragged and rotting,
With still red tendons curled. Twice they saw
The whole delicate skeletons with the hard
Hornlike feet peacefully displayed, and there
A loud few flies buzzed on the torn meat
And dishevelled feathers; a sick and wrong
Smell mingled with the heat of the salt wind.

Silence strangely was twisted there   20
By the voices of the children, by

The Lives of Gulls and Children   **116**

The outcries of the living gulls aloft
Swinging over the wash and rush of the sea
Between the heat of the sand and the blind sun of
    noon.

They saw there a great gull dying,
Huddled in the sun and shuddering out
Now and again a heavy wing in cold
Effortful motion; he stared at them
Out of a steady and majestic eye
Like a sun part baffled in cloud,   30
So rheumed over with the morning of death.

They would have reached out hands to him
To comfort him in that human kind
They just were learning—how anything alive,
They thought, hated loneliness most; but he,
A grim great-uncle with a cane, struck out,
Sullen and weakly fierce, with hooked beak and a
    claw.
He would have flown, but had not strength to rise,
Could not even, ridiculous, waddle away.

The children watched him for a moment more,   40
But at a distance, and did not see him die;
For he, making his death, would out-endure
What interest they had, who, being humankind,
Had homes to go to, and a bed this side of death.

But they knew the Atlantic kind he was,
And for this moment saw him swaying
In the grey dark above the cold sea miles,
Wingtips ticking the spray of the slow waves,
Leaning on the unhavening air the dangerous
Sustaining of his own breastbone; they knew   50
The indifference of time dragging him down.
And when after silence they turned away,
"No one has ever been here before,"

They cried, "no one, no one, no one."
Their mournful word went out, no one,
Along the shore, now that they turned for home
Bearing the lonely pride of those who die,
And paced by the sweet shrieking of the quick.

—HOWARD NEMEROV

The Lives of Gulls and Children   118

section eight.

Here the poets respond to two inexorable realities
—fate and time. They counter time with art,
and fate with persistence and fortitude.

THE CONVERGENCE OF THE TWAIN
(Lines on the loss of the *Titanic*)

I.
In a solitude of the sea
Deep from human vanity,
And the Pride of Life that planned her, stilly couches
she.

II.
Steel chambers, late the pyres
Of her salamandrine fires,
Cold currents thrid, and turn to rhythmic tidal
lyres.

III.
Over the mirrors meant
To glass the opulent
The sea-worm crawls—grotesque, slimed, dumb,
indifferent.

IV.
Jewels in joy designed   10
To ravish the sensuous mind
Lie lightless, all their sparkles bleared and black and
blind.

V.
Dim moon-eyed fishes near
Gaze at the gilded gear
And query: "What does this vaingloriousness
down here?" . . .

VI.
Well: while was fashioning
This creature of cleaving wing,
The Immanent Will that stirs and urges everything

VII.
Prepared a sinister mate
For her—so gaily great—   20
A Shape of Ice, for the time far and dissociate.

VIII.
And as the smart ship grew
In stature, grace, and hue,
In shadowy silent distance grew the Iceberg too.

IX.
Alien they seemed to be:
No mortal eye could see
The intimate welding of their later history,

X.
Or sign that they were bent
By paths coincident
On being anon twin halves of one august event,   30

XI.
Till the Spinner of the Years
Said "Now!" And each one hears,
And consummation comes, and jars two
hemispheres.

—THOMAS HARDY

The Convergence of the Twain   **120**

RES PUBLICA

They bled a bullock, and stripped the hide,
Cast to the dogs what they could not use;
Tanned the skin that the sun had dried,
And made the leather for Caesar's shoes.

A shivering lamb was shorn in Spain;
The wool was teased and combed and dressed.
They washed it clean of the pasture stain,
And wove the toga for Caesar's breast.

A pig that rooted acorns saw
The shrub resent as they plucked the bough,   10
And watched the shadows of men withdraw
Bearing the laurel for Caesar's brow.

They dug the metal to fill the mould,
And fed the flame in a place apart;
Ground the edge when the steel was cold,
And made the dagger for Caesar's heart.

—J. A. R. McKELLAR

DEATH THE LEVELLER

The glories of our blood and state
 Are shadows, not substantial things;
There is no armour against fate;
 Death lays his icy hand on kings:
  Sceptre and Crown
  Must tumble down,
And in the dust be equal made
With the poor crooked scythe and spade.

Some men with swords may reap the field,

And plant fresh laurels where they kill: 10
But their strong nerves at last must yield;
    They tame but one another still:
        Early or late
        They stoop to fate,
And must give up their murmuring breath
When they, pale captives, creep to death.

The garlands wither on your brow;
    Then boast no more your mighty deeds;
Upon Death's purple altar now
    See where the victor-victim bleeds: 20
        Your heads must come
        To the cold tomb;
Only the actions of the just
Smell sweet, and blossom in their dust.

                          —JAMES SHIRLEY

SEE WHERE CAPELLA
WITH HER GOLDEN KIDS

See where Capella[1] with her golden kids
Grazes the slope between the east and north:
Thus when the builders of the pyramids
Flung down their tools at nightfall and poured forth
Homeward to supper and a poor man's bed,
Shortening the road with friendly jest and slur,
The risen She-Goat showing blue and red
Climbed the clear dusk, and three stars followed her.
Safe in their linen and their spices lie
The kings of Egypt; even as long ago   10
Under these constellations, with long eye
And scented limbs they slept, and feared no foe.
Their will was law; their will was not to die.
And so they had their way; or nearly so.

                    —EDNA ST. VINCENT MILLAY

CITIES AND THRONES AND POWERS

Cities and Thrones and Powers
   Stand in Time's eye,
Almost as long as flowers,
   Which daily die:
But, as new buds put forth
   To glad new men,
Out of the spent and unconsidered Earth,
   The Cities rise again.

This season's Daffodil,
   She never hears,   10
What change, what chance, what chill,
   Cut down last year's;
But with bold countenance,
   And knowledge small,
Esteems her seven days' continuance,
   To be perpetual.

So Time that is o'er-kind,
   To all that be,
Ordains us e'en as blind,
   As bold as she: 20
That in our very death,
   And burial sure,
Shadow to shadow, well persuaded, saith,
   "See how our works endure!"
                    —RUDYARD KIPLING

VAE VICTIS

The Romans have invaded us again,—
That decadent nation, with the melancholy
Under the ostentation and the bronze,
Misgivers, dressed in attitudes of scorn,

Corrupted by their own imposing folly,
The bands and banners, cruelty and games,
Victorious over green battalions,
Summer's luxurious easy army slain.

They line our highways, confiscate our corn,
Possess our fields and set our woods in flames.   10
Each year they come, each year they flash and shine,
Proud in imperial purple, orange, gold,
Maroon, magenta, madder, carmine, wine,
Vermilion, umber; arrogant and bold.

Each year, some morning finds them driven forth
In panic by a rumor from the north,
Their camps forsaken, flying for their lives
Before the keen barbarians, armed with knives,
The fierce and terrible Scythians,[1] whose breath
Sets in the crimson vein the blue of death.   20

Alarm, alarm! The fires burn black by dawn,
The wavering legions vanish and are gone,
Leaving no monument, no trace to mark
The mutinous disorder in the dark
Except the hue of blood, the deep red stain
Where some courageous officer was slain,
Or, it may be, a cloak of scarlet, found
Under a maple, on the frozen ground.

—ROLFE HUMPHRIES

POLO GROUNDS[1]

Time is of the essence. This is a highly skilled
And beautiful mystery. Three or four seconds only
From the time that Riggs connects till he reaches
        first,
And in those seconds Jurges goes to his right,
Comes up with the ball, tosses to Witek at second

For the force on Reese, Witek to Mize at first,
In time for the out—a double play.

(Red Barber crescendo. Crowd noises, obbligato;
Scattered staccatos from the peanut boys,
Loud in the lull, as the teams are changing sides) . . .   10

Hubbell takes the sign, nods, pumps, delivers—
A foul into the stands. Dunn takes a new ball out,
Hands it to Danning, who throws it down to Werber;
Werber takes off his glove, rubs the ball briefly,
Tosses it over to Hub, who goes to the rosin bag,
Takes the sign from Danning, pumps, delivers—
Low, outside, ball three. Danning goes to the mound,
Says something to Hub, Dunn brushes off the plate,
Adams starts throwing in the Giant bullpen,
Hub takes the sign from Danning, pumps, delivers,   20
Camilli gets hold of it, a *long* fly to the outfield,
Ott goes back, back, back, against the wall, gets
     under it,
Pounds his glove, and takes it for the out.
That's all for the Dodgers. . . .

Time is of the essence. The rhythms break,
More varied and subtle than any kind of dance;
Movement speeds up or lags. The ball goes out
In sharp and angular drives, or long, slow arcs,
Comes in again controlled and under aim;
The players wheel or spurt, race, stoop, slide, halt,   30
Shift imperceptibly to new positions,
Watching the signs, according to the batter,
The score, the inning. Time is of the essence.

Time is of the essence. Remember Terry?
Remember Stonewall Jackson, Lindstrom, Frisch,
When they were good? Remember Long George
     Kelly?
Remember John McGraw and Benny Kauff?

Polo Grounds   125

Remember Bridwell, Tenney, Merkle, Youngs,
Chief Myers, Big Jeff Tesreau, Shufflin' Phil?
Remember Matthewson, and Ames, and Donlin,   40
Buck Ewing, Rusie, Smiling Mickey Welch?
Remember a left-handed catcher named Jack Hum-
    phries,
Who sometimes played the outfield, in '83?

Time is of the essence. The shadow moves
From the plate to the box, from the box to second
    base,
From second to the outfield, to the bleachers.

Time is of the essence. The crowd and players
Are the same age always, but the man in the crowd
Is older every season. Come on, play ball!
                                    —ROLFE HUMPHRIES

SHALL I COMPARE
THEE TO A SUMMER'S DAY?

Shall I compare thee to a summer's day?
Thou art more lovely and more temperate:
Rough winds do shake the darling buds of May,
And summer's lease[1] hath all too short a date:
Sometime too hot the eye of heaven shines,
And often is his gold complexion dimmed:
And every fair from fair[2] sometime declines,
By chance, or nature's changing course, untrimmed.[3]
But thy eternal summer shall not fade,
Nor lose possession of that fair thou ow'st,[4]   10
Nor shall death brag thou wander'st in his shade,
When in eternal lines to time thou grow'st;
    So long as men can breathe, or eyes can see,
    So long lives this, and this gives life to thee.
                              —WILLIAM SHAKESPEARE

TO THE STONE-CUTTERS

Stone-cutters fighting time with marble, you fore-
    defeated
Challengers of oblivion,
Eat cynical earnings, knowing rock splits, records fall
    down,
The square-limbed Roman letters
Scale in the thaws, wear in the rain. The poet as well
Builds his monument mockingly;
For man will be blotted out, the blithe earth die, the
    brave sun
Die blind and blacken to the heart:
Yet stones have stood for a thousand years, and
    pained thoughts found
The honey of peace in old poems.   10
                        —ROBINSON JEFFERS

THE STATUE

Short, husky, black and brown with dust and sweat
The quarry men, whose bar and sledge have pried
The marble loose, stand back to watch it drawn
Down the rough skidroad from the mountainside,

Out of its first exposure, heading toward
A new erosion, where a mind, an eye,
And something called imagination, wait
To wear it down, before the hands dare try

To grasp and lift the chisel and the maul,
One man's complete employment now,—observe   10
How stone is dressed in nakedness, how steel
With sharp straight edge brings out the bevelled
    curve.

One man does this, who stops at times, and frowns,
Or hums himself a little tune that goes,
When all goes well, *The more the marble wastes,*
The more it wastes, the more the statue grows.

Finished, at last (he thinks) and sold, and set
In some appropriate spot, a colonnade
Or Syracusan[1] grove, where oranges
Are balls of sun among the globes of shade.   20

Here, like its owner's fortune, just a trace
Too new for dignity, the statue stands,
Almost a masterpiece, requiring still
Some final touch, the work of other hands.

And these are given; wind and rain and sun,
Time and the weather, infinitely slow,
Patient through generations, waste and wear,
Correct the marble, make the figure grow,

So that tradition, anciency, and grace
Are added by subtraction, and the pure   30
Symbol from image forms, along whose base
Runs the new rune—*See how our works endure.*

Endure, disintegrate, and, even beyond
Disintegration, live in long renown:
After the vandals come, lop off the limbs,
Hack at the head and helmet, topple down

The mutilated torso, drag it off
Aboard a ship, to cast it in the seas,
Granted its last perfection, men recall
Its glory in one word—Praxiteles.[2]   40

—ROLFE HUMPHRIES

THE BROKEN DIKE,
THE LEVEE WASHED AWAY

The broken dike, the levee washed away,
The good fields flooded and the cattle drowned,

Estranged and treacherous all the faithful ground,
And nothing left but floating disarray
Of tree and home uprooted—was this the day
Man dropped upon his shadow without a sound
And died, having labored well and having found
His burden heavier than a quilt of clay?
No, no. I saw him when the sun had set
In water, leaning on his single oar   10
Above his garden faintly glimmering yet—
There bulked the plow, here washed the updrifted
    weeds—
And scull across his roof and make for shore,
With twisted face and pocket full of seeds.

—EDNA ST. VINCENT MILLAY

THE CHOICE [1]

I have known one bound to a bed by wrist and ankle,
Scarred by the whips of a wasting ache,
Who, at the point of entering of the needle,
Looked once around to take
The final view, then spoke;
The echo of that terribly witty joke
Pursued the surgeon to his home in Kew,
Deafened a nurse all night, and leaden lay
On the heart of a thick-skinned anesthetist
Long after they'd dispatched his ended clay.   10

That one lies in Oxford and is its earth.
Also, a bright-eyed woman in Germany,
In a sightless trap, far below ground,
Of which another held the key,
Surveyed without visible alarm
Or twitching of a pinioned arm
The instruments set out upon a table;
Then from her mouth there flowed a resolute
Stream of satire deliciously edged until
The tormentor tormented stopped it with a boot.   20

She fell as ash, not bones, in Dachau fields.
All brave men breathe her when the wind
Blows east from Danube. And Tom Caine,
When the *Imperial* was mined
And water had flooded all but the wireless room,
Spoke without audible gloom
From fifty fathoms down for fifteen hours
To his messmates on land, told several stories,
Then to a doctor carefully described
Asphyxiation's onset and his doom.   30

He is grown water and surrounds the pole.
If ever you dip a cup in any sea
Tom Caine is in it somewhere. On the whole
Men die asleep or else disgracefully;
But not all men. Perhaps we are never,
By any average mountain, wood, or river,
More than a heart's breadth from the dust
Of one who laughed with nothing left to lose.
Who saw the joke beneath the mammoth's foot?
And what shall I choose, if I am free to choose?   40

—HILARY CORKE

section nine.

In these six poems the poet expresses his love of home
and of the values that home represents:
continuity and security.

A LONDON THOROUGHFARE TWO A. M.

They have watered the street,
It shines in the glare of lamps,
Cold, white lamps,
And lies
Like a slow-moving river,
Barred with silver and black.
Cabs go down it,
One,
And then another.
Between them I hear the shuffling of feet,   10
Tramps doze on the window-ledges,
Night walkers pass along the sidewalks.
The city is squalid and sinister,
With the silver-barred street in the midst,
Slow-moving,
A river leading nowhere.

Opposite my window,
The moon cuts,
Clear and round,
Through the plum-colored night.   20
She cannot light the city;
It is too bright.
It has white lamps,
And glitters coldly.

I stand in the window and watch the moon.
She is thin and lusterless,
But I love her.
I know the moon,
And this is an alien city.

—AMY LOWELL

THE LONG VOYAGE

Not that the pines were darker there,
nor mid-May dogwood brighter there,
nor swifts more swift in summer air;
    it was my own country,

having its thunderclap of spring,
its long midsummer ripening,
its corn hoar-stiff at harvesting,
    almost like any country,

yet being mine; its face, its speech,
its hills bent low within my reach,   10
its river birch and upland beech
    were mine, of my own country.

Now the dark waters at the bow
fold back, like earth against the plow;
foam brightens like the dogwood now
    at home, in my own country.

—MALCOLM COWLEY

EXILED

Searching my heart for its true sorrow,
   This is the thing I find to be:
That I am weary of words and people,
   Sick of the city, wanting the sea;

Exiled   **132**

Wanting the sticky, salty sweetness
  Of the strong wind and shattered spray;
Wanting the loud sound and the soft sound
  Of the big surf that breaks all day.

Always before about my dooryard,
  Marking the reach of the winter sea,   10
Rooted in sand and dragging driftwood,
  Straggled the purple wild sweet pea;

Always I climbed the wave at morning,
  Shook the sand from my shoes at night,
That now am caught beneath great buildings,
  Stricken with noise, confused with light.

If I could hear the green piles groaning
  Under the windy wooden piers,
See again the bobbing barrels,
  And the black sticks that fence the weirs,   20

If I could see the weedy mussels
  Crusting the wrecked and rotting hulls,
Hear once again the hungry crying
  Overhead, of the wheeling gulls,

Feel once again the shanty straining
  Under the turning of the tide,
Fear once again the rising freshet,
  Dread the bell in the fog outside,

I should be happy—that was happy
  All day long on the coast of Maine.   30
I have a need to hold and handle
  Shells and anchors and ships again!

I should be happy, that am happy
  Never at all since I came here.
I am too long away from water.
  I have a need of water near.

                        —EDNA ST. VINCENT MILLAY

THE LAND

When Julius Fabricius, Sub-Prefect of the Weald,
In the days of Diocletian owned our Lower River-field,
He called to him Hobdenius—a Briton of the Clay,
Saying: "What about that River-piece for layin' in
 to hay?"

And the aged Hobden answered: "I remember as a
 lad
My father told your father that she wanted dreenin'[1]
 bad.
An' the more that you neeglect her the less you'll get
 her clean.
Have it jest *as* you've a mind to, but, if I was you,
 I'd dreen."

So they drained it long and crossways in the lavish
 Roman style—
Still we find among the river-drift their flakes of
 ancient tile,
And in drouthy middle August, when the bones of
 meadows show,
We can trace the lines they followed sixteen hundred
 years ago.

Then Julius Fabricius died as even Prefects do,
And after certain centuries, Imperial Rome died too.
Then did robbers enter Britain from across the
 Northern main
And our Lower River-field was won by Ogier the
 Dane.

Well could Ogier work his war-boat—well could Ogier
 wield his brand—
Much he knew of foaming waters—not so much of
 farming land.

So he called to him a Hobden of the old unaltered
  blood,
Saying: "What about that River-piece, she doesn't
  look no good?"   20

And that aged Hobden answered: " 'Tain't for *me* to
  interfere,
But I've known that bit o' meadow now for five and
  fifty year.
Have it *jest* as you've a mind to, but I've proved it time
  on time,
If you want to change her nature you have *got* to give
  her lime!"

Ogier sent his wains² to Lewes, twenty hours' solemn
  walk,
And drew back great abundance of the cool, grey,
  healing chalk.
And old Hobden spread it broadcast, never heeding
  what was in 't.
Which is why in cleaning ditches, now and then we
  find a flint.

Ogier died. His sons grew English—Anglo-Saxon was
  their name—
Till out of blossomed Normandy another pirate came;   30
For Duke William conquered England and divided
  with his men,
And our Lower River-field he gave to William of
  Warenne.

But the Brook (you know her habit) rose one rainy
  autumn night
And tore down sodden flitches³ of the bank to left and
  right.
So, said William to his Bailiff as they rode their
  dripping rounds:
"Hob, what about that River-bit—the Brook's got up
  no bounds?"

The Land   **135**

And that aged Hobden answered: "'Tain't my business to advise,
But ye might ha' known 'twould happen from the way the valley lies.
Where ye can't hold back the water you must try and save the sile.[4]
Hev it jest as you've a *mind* to, but, if I was you, I'd spile!"[5]   40

They spiled along the water-course with trunks of willow-trees
And planks of elms behind 'em and immortal oaken knees.
And when the spates of Autumn whirl the gravel-beds away
You can see their faithful fragments iron-hard in iron clay.

∙ ∙

Georgii Quinti Anno Sexto,[6] I, who own the River-field,
Am fortified with title-deeds, attested, signed and sealed,
Guaranteeing me, my assigns, my executors and heirs
All sorts of powers and profits which—are neither mine nor theirs.

I have rights of chase and warren,[7] as my dignity requires.
I can fish—but Hobden tickles.[8] I can shoot—but Hobden wires.[9]   50
I repair, but he reopens, certain gaps which, men allege,
Have been used by every Hobden since a Hobden swapped a hedge.[10]

Shall I dog his morning progress o'er the track-betraying dew?

Demand his dinner-basket into which my pheasant
    flew?
Confiscate his evening faggot[11] under which the
    conies[12] ran,
And summons him to judgment? I would sooner
    summons Pan.[13]

His dead are in the churchyard—thirty generations
    laid.
Their names were old in history when Domesday
    Book[14] was made.
And the passion and the piety and prowess of his line
Have seeded, rooted, fruited in some land the Law   60
    calls mine.

Not for any beast that burrows, not for any bird that
    flies,
Would I lose his large sound council, miss his keen
    amending eyes.
He is bailiff, woodman, wheelwright, field-surveyor,
    engineer,
And if flagrantly a poacher—'tain't for me to
    interfere.

"Hob, what about that River-bit?" I turn to him
    again,
With Fabricius and Ogier and William of Warenne.
"Hev it jest as you've a mind to, *but*"—and here he
    takes command.
For whoever pays the taxes old Mus'[15] Hobden owns
    the land.

                —RUDYARD KIPLING

SOLITUDE

Happy the man whose wish and care
A few paternal acres bound,
Content to breathe his native air
    In his own ground.

Whose herds with milk, whose fields with bread,
Whose flocks supply him with attire;
Whose trees in summer yield him shade,
    In winter fire.

Blest, who can unconcern'dly find
Hours, days, and years slide soft away   10
In health of body, peace of mind;
    Quiet by day,

Sound sleep by night; study and ease
Together mixed; sweet recreation;
And innocence, which most does please
    With meditation.

Thus let me live, unseen, unknown;
Thus unlamented let me die;
Steal from the world, and not a stone
    Tell where I lie.   20

                            —ALEXANDER POPE

THE DYKES

We have no heart for the fishing, we have no hand
    for the oar—
All that our fathers taught us of old pleases us now
    no more;
All that our own hearts bid us believe we doubt where
    we do not deny—
There is no proof in the bread we eat or rest in the
    toil we ply.

Look you, our foreshore stretches far through sea-
    gate, dyke, and groin[1]—
Made land all, that our fathers made, where the flats
    and the fairway join.

The Dykes   **138**

They forced the sea a sea-league back. They died, and
    their work stood fast.
We were born to peace in the lee of the dykes, but the
    time of our peace is past.

Far off, the full tide clambers and slips, mouthing
    and testing all,
Nipping the flanks of the water-gates, baying along
    the wall;   10
Turning the shingle, returning the shingle, changing
    the set of the sand . . .
We are too far from the beach, men say, to know how
    the outworks stand.

So we come down, uneasy, to look, uneasily pacing
    the beach.
These are the dykes our fathers made: we have never
    known a breach.
Time and again has the gale blown by and we were
    not afraid;
Now we come only to look at the dykes—at the dykes
    our fathers made.

O'er the marsh where the homesteads cower apart the
    harried sunlight flies,
Shifts and considers, wanes and recovers, scatters
    and sickens and dies—
An evil ember bedded in ash—a spark blown west by
    the wind . . .
We are surrendered to night and the sea—the gale
    and the tide behind!   20

At the bridge of the lower saltings[2] the cattle gather
    and blare,
Roused by the feet of running men, dazed by the
    lantern glare.
Unbar and let them away for their lives—the levels
    drown as they stand,

The Dykes   **139**

Where the flood-wash forces the sluices[8] aback and
    the ditches deliver inland.

Ninefold deep to the top of the dykes the galloping
    breakers stride,
And their overcarried spray is a sea—a sea on the
    landward side.
Coming, like stallions they paw with their hooves,
    going they snatch with their teeth,
Till the bents[4] and the furze[5] and the sand are
    dragged out, and the old-time hurdles[6] beneath!

Bid men gather fuel for fire, the tar, the oil, and the
    tow[7]—
Flame we shall need, not smoke, in the dark if the
    riddled sea-banks go.   30
Bid the ringers watch in the tower (who knows how
    the dawn shall prove?)
Each with his rope between his feet and the trem-
    bling bells above.

Now we can only wait till the day, wait and apportion
    our shame.
These are the dykes our fathers left, but we would not
    look to the same.
Time and again were we warned of the dykes, time
    and again we delayed:
Now, it may fall, we have slain our sons, as our
    fathers we have betrayed.

. . . .

Walking along the wreck of the dykes, watching the
    work of the seas!
These were the dykes our fathers made to our great
    profit and ease.
But the peace is gone and the profit is gone, and the
    old sure day withdrawn . . .
That our own houses show as strange when we come
    back in the dawn!   40
                      —RUDYARD KIPLING

section ten.

First the beauty of winter;
then the inevitable kinship of winter
with old age, loneliness, and death.

LONDON SNOW

When men were all asleep the snow came flying,
In large white flakes falling on the city brown,
Stealthily and perpetually settling and loosely lying,
    Hushing the latest traffic of the drowsy town;
Deadening, muffling, stifling its murmurs failing;
Lazily and incessantly floating down and down:
    Silently sifting and veiling road, roof and railing;
Hiding difference, making unevenness even,
Into angles and crevices softly drifting and sailing.
    All night it fell, and when full inches seven   10
It lay in the depth of its uncompacted lightness,
The clouds blew off from a high and frosty heaven;
    And all woke earlier for the unaccustomed bright-
        ness
Of the winter dawning, the strange unheavenly
        glare:
The eye marvelled—marvelled at the dazzling white-
        ness;
    The ear hearkened to the stillness of the solemn
        air;
No sound of wheel rumbling nor of foot falling,
And the busy morning cries came thin and spare.
    Then boys I heard, as they went to school, calling,
They gathered up the crystal manna to freeze   20

Their tongues with tasting, their hands with snow-
        balling;
    Or rioted in a drift, plunging up to the knees;
Or peering up from under the white-mossed wonder,
"O look at the trees!" they cried, "O look at the trees!"
    With lessened load a few carts creak and blunder,
Following along the white deserted way,
A country company long dispersed asunder:
    When now already the sun, in pale display
Standing by Paul's high dome, spread forth below
His sparkling beams, and awoke the stir of the day.   30
    For now doors open, and war is waged with the
        snow;
And trains of somber men, past tale of number,
Tread long brown paths, as toward their toil they go:
    But even for them awhile no cares encumber
Their minds diverted; the daily word is unspoken,
The daily thoughts of labor and sorrow slumber
At the sight of the beauty that greets them, for the
        charm they have broken.
                                        —ROBERT BRIDGES

AN OLD MAN'S WINTER NIGHT

All out of doors looked darkly in at him
Through the thin frost, almost in separate stars,
That gathers on the pane in empty rooms.
What kept his eyes from giving back the gaze
Was the lamp tilted near them in his hand.
What kept him from remembering the need
That brought him to that creaking room was age.
He stood with barrels round him—at a loss.

And having scared the cellar under him
In clomping here, he scared it once again   10
In clomping off;—and scared the outer night,
Which has its sounds, familiar, like the roar

Of trees and crack of branches, common things,
But nothing so like beating on a box.
A light he was to no one but himself
Where now he sat, concerned with he knew what,
A quiet light, and then not even that.
He consigned to the moon, such as she was,
So late-arising, to the broken moon
As better than the sun in any case   20
For such a charge, his snow upon the roof,
His icicles along the wall to keep;
And slept. The log that shifted with a jolt
Once in the stove, disturbed him and he shifted,
And eased his heavy breathing, but still slept.
One aged man—one man—can't keep a house,
A farm, a countryside, or if he can,
It's thus he does it of a winter night.

—ROBERT FROST

MR. FLOOD'S PARTY

Old Eben Flood, climbing alone one night
Over the hill between the town below
And the forsaken upland hermitage
That held as much as he should ever know
On earth again of home, paused warily.
The road was his with not a native near;
And Eben, having leisure, said aloud,
For no man else in Tilbury Town to hear:

"Well, Mr. Flood, we have the harvest moon
Again, and we may not have many more;   10
The bird is on the wing, the poet says,
And you and I have said it here before.
Drink to the bird." He raised up to the light
The jug that he had gone so far to fill,
And answered huskily: "Well, Mr. Flood,
Since you propose it, I believe I will."

Mr. Flood's Party   **143**

Alone, as if enduring to the end
A valiant armor of scarred hopes outworn,
He stood there in the middle of the road
Like Roland's ghost winding a silent horn.[1]   20
Below him, in the town among the trees,
Where friends of other days had honored him,
A phantom salutation of the dead
Rang thinly till old Eben's eyes were dim.

Then, as a mother lays her sleeping child
Down tenderly, fearing it may awake,
He set the jug down slowly at his feet
With trembling care, knowing that most things
      break;
And only when assured that on firm earth
It stood, as the uncertain lives of men   30
Assuredly did not, he paced away,
And with his hand extended paused again:

"Well, Mr. Flood, we have not met like this
In a long time; and many a change has come
To both of us, I fear, since last it was
We had a drop together. Welcome home!"
Convivially returning with himself,
Again he raised the jug up to the light;
And with an acquiescent quaver said:
"Well, Mr. Flood, if you insist, I might.   40

"Only a very little, Mr. Flood—
For auld lang syne. No more, sir; that will do."
So, for the time, apparently it did,
And Eben evidently thought so too;
For soon amid the silver loneliness
Of night he lifted up his voice and sang,
Secure, with only two moons listening,
Until the whole harmonious landscape rang—

"For auld lang syne." The weary throat gave out,
The last word wavered, and the song was done,   50

Mr. Flood's Party   **144**

He raised again the jug regretfully
And shook his head, and was again alone.
There was not much that was ahead of him,
And there was nothing in the town below—
Where strangers would have shut the many doors
That many friends had opened long ago.

—E. A. ROBINSON

ISAAC AND ARCHIBALD

Isaac and Archibald were two old men.
I knew them, and I may have laughed at them
A little; but I must have honored them
For they were old, and they were good to me.

I do not think of either of them now,
Without remembering, infallibly,
A journey that I made one afternoon
With Isaac to find out what Archibald
Was doing with his oats. It was high time
Those oats were cut, said Isaac; and he feared   10
That Archibald—well, he could never feel
Quite sure of Archibald. Accordingly
The good old man invited me—that is,
Permitted me—to go along with him;
And I, with a small boy's adhesiveness
To competent old age, got up and went.
I do not know that I cared overmuch
For Archibald's or anybody's oats,
But Archibald was quite another thing,
And Isaac yet another; and the world   20
Was wide, and there was gladness everywhere.
We walked together down the River Road
With all the warmth and wonder of the land
Around us, and the wayside flash of leaves,—
And Isaac said the day was glorious;
But somewhere at the end of the first mile

I found that I was figuring to find
How long those ancient legs of his would keep
The pace that he had set for them. The sun
Was hot, and I was ready to sweat blood;　　　　　　30
But Isaac, for aught I could make of him,
Was cool to his hat-band. So I said then
With a dry gasp of affable despair,
Something about the scorching days we have
In August without knowing it sometimes;
But Isaac said the day was like a dream,
And praised the Lord, and talked about the breeze.
I made a fair confession of the breeze,
And crowded casually on his thought
The nearness of a profitable nook
That I could see. First I was half inclined　　　　　　40
To caution him that he was growing old,
But something that was not compassion soon
Made plain the folly of all subterfuge.
Isaac was old, but not so old as that.

So I proposed, without an overture,
That we be seated in the shade a while,
And Isaac made no murmur. Soon the talk
Was turned on Archibald, and I began
To feel some premonitions of a kind
That only childhood knows; for the old man　　　　　　50
Had looked at me and clutched me with his eye,
And asked if I had ever noticed things.
I told him that I could not think of them,
And I knew then, by the frown that left his face
Unsatisfied, that I had injured him.
"My good young friend," he said, "you cannot feel
What I have seen so long. You have the eyes—
Oh, yes—but you have not the other things:
The sight within that never will deceive,
You do not know—you have no right to know;　　　　　　60
The twilight warning of experience,
The singular idea of loneliness,—
These are not yours. But they have long been mine,

And they have shown me now for seven years
That Archibald is changing. It is not
So much that he should come to his last hand,
And leave the game, and go the old way down;
But I have known him in and out so long,
And I have seen so much of good in him
That other men have shared and have not seen,   70
And I have gone so far through thick and thin,
Through cold and fire with him, that now it brings
To this old heart of mine an ache that you
Have not yet lived enough to know about.
But even unto you, and your boy's faith,
Your freedom, and your untried confidence,
A time will come to find out what it means
To know that you are losing what was yours,
To know that you are being left behind;
And then the long contempt of innocence—   80
God bless you, boy!—don't think the worse of it
Because an old man chatters in the shade—
Will all be like a story you have read
In childhood and remembered for the pictures.
And when the best friend of your life goes down,
When first you know in him the slackening
That comes, and coming always tells the end,—
Now in a common word that would have passed
Uncaught from any other lips than his,
Now in some trivial act of every day,   90
Done as he might have done it all along
But for a twinging little difference
That nips you like a squirrel's teeth—oh, yes,
Then you will understand it well enough.
But oftener it comes in other ways;
It comes without your knowing when it comes;
You know that he is changing, and you know
That he is going—just as I know now
That Archibald is going, and that I
Am staying. . . . Look at me, my boy,   100
And when the time shall come for you to see
That I must follow after him, try then

To think of me, to bring me back again,
Just as I was today. Think of the place
Where we are sitting now, and think of me—
Think of old Isaac as you knew him then,
When you set out with him in August once
To see old Archibald."—The words come back
Almost as Isaac must have uttered them,
And there comes with them a dry memory   110
Of something in my throat that would not move.

If you had asked me then to tell just why
I made so much of Isaac and the things
He said, I should have gone far for an answer;
For I knew it was not sorrow that I felt,
Whatever I may have wished it, or tried then
To make myself believe. My mouth was full
Of words, and they would have been comforting
To Isaac, spite of my twelve years, I think;
But there was not in me the willingness   120
To speak them out. Therefore I watched the ground;
And I was wondering what made the Lord
Create a thing so nervous as an ant,
When Isaac, with commendable unrest,
Ordained that we should take the road again—
For it was yet three miles to Archibald's,
And one to the first pump. I felt relieved
All over when the old man told me that;
I felt that he had stilled a fear of mine
That those extremities of heat and cold   130
Which he had long gone through with Archibald
Had made the man impervious to both;
But Isaac had a desert somewhere in him,
And at the pump he thanked God for all things
That He had put on earth for men to drink,
And he drank well,—so well that I proposed
That we go slowly lest I learn too soon
The bitterness of being left behind,
And all those other things. That was a joke

To Isaac, and it pleased him very much;   140
And that pleased me—for I was twelve years old.

At the end of an hour's walking after that
The cottage of old Archibald appeared.
Little and white and high on a smooth round hill
It stood, with hackmatacks and appletrees
Before it, and a big barn-roof beyond;
And over the place—trees, houses, fields and all—
Hovered an air of still simplicity
And a fragrance of old summers—the old style
That lives the while it passes. I dare say   150
That I was lightly conscious of all this
When Isaac, of a sudden, stopped himself,
And for the long first quarter of a minute
Gazed with incredulous eyes, forgetful quite
Of breezes and of me and of all else
Under the scorching sun but a smooth-cut field,
Faint yellow in the distance. I was young,
But there were a few things that I could see,
And this was one of them.—"Well, well!" said he;
And "Archibald will be surprised, I think,"   160
Said I. But all my childhood subtlety
Was lost on Isaac, for he strode along
Like something out of Homer—powerful
And awful on the wayside, so I thought.
Also I thought how good it was to be
So near the end of my short-legged endeavor
To keep the pace with Isaac for five miles.

Hardly had we turned in from the main road
When Archibald, with one hand on his back
And the other clutching his huge-headed cane,   170
Came limping down to meet us.—"Well! well! well!"
Said he; and then he looked at my red face,
All streaked with dust and sweat, and shook my
        hand,
And said it must have been a right smart walk

That we had had that day from Tilbury Town.—
"Magnificent," said Isaac; and he told
About the beautiful west wind there was
Which cooled and clarified the atmosphere.
"You must have made it with your legs, I guess,"
Said Archibald; and Isaac humored him   180
With one of those infrequent smiles of his
Which he kept in reserve, apparently,
For Archibald alone. "But why," said he,
"Should Providence have cider in the world
If not for such an afternoon as this?"
And Archibald, with a soft light in his eyes,
Replied that if he chose to go down cellar,
There he would find eight barrels—one of which
Was newly tapped, he said, and to his taste
An honor to the fruit. Isaac approved   190
Most heartily of that, and guided us
Forthwith, as if his venerable feet
Were measuring the turf in his own door-yard,
Straight to the open rollway. Down we went,
Out of the fiery sunshine to the gloom,
Grateful and half sepulchral, where we found
The barrels, like eight potent sentinels,
Close ranged along the wall. From one of them
A bright pine spile stuck out alluringly,
And on the black flat stone, just under it,   200
Glimmered a late-spilled proof that Archibald
Had spoken from unfeigned experience.
There was a fluted antique water-glass
Close by, and in it, prisoned, or at rest,
There was a cricket, of the brown soft sort
That feeds on darkness. Isaac turned him out,
And touched him with his thumb to make him jump,
And then composedly pulled out the plug
With such a practiced hand that scarce a drop
Did even touch his fingers. Then he drank   210
And smacked his lips with a slow patronage
And looked along the line of barrels there
With a pride that may have been forgetfulness

That they were Archibald's and not his own.
"I never twist a spigot nowadays,"
He said, and raised the glass up to the light,
"But I thank God for orchards." And that glass
Was filled repeatedly for the same hand
Before I thought it worthwhile to discern
Again that I was young, and that old age, 220
With all his woes, had some advantages.

"Now, Archibald," said Isaac, when we stood
Outside again, "I have it in my mind
That I shall take a sort of little walk—
To stretch my legs and see what you are doing.
You stay and rest your back and tell the boy
A story: Tell him all about the time
In Stafford's cabin forty years ago,
When four of us were snowed up for ten days
With only one dried haddock. Tell him all 230
About it, and be wary of your back.
Now I will go along."—I looked up then
At Archibald, and as I looked I saw
Just how his nostrils widened once or twice
And then grew narrow. I can hear today
The way the old man chuckled to himself—
Not wholesomely, not wholly to convince
Another of his mirth,—as I can hear
The lonely sigh that followed.—But at length
He said: "The orchard now's the place for us; 240
We may find something like an apple there,
And we shall have the shade, at any rate."
So there we went and there we laid ourselves
Where the sun could not reach us; and I champed
A dozen of worm-blighted astrakhans
While Archibald said nothing—merely told
The tale of Stafford's cabin, which was good,
Though "master chilly"—after his own phrase—
Even for a day like that. But other thoughts
Were moving in his mind, imperative, 250
And writhing to be spoken: I could see

Isaac and Archibald   **151**

The glimmer of them in a glance or two,
Cautious, or else unconscious, that he gave
Over his shoulder: . . . "Stafford and the rest—
But that's an old song now, and Archibald
And Isaac are old men. Remember, boy,
That we are old. Whatever we have gained,
Or lost, or thrown away, we are old men.
You look before you and we look behind,
And we are playing life out in the shadow—   260
But that's not all of it. The sunshine lights
A good road yet before us if we look,
And we are doing that when least we know it;
For both of us are children of the sun,
Like you, and like the weed there at your feet.
The shadow calls us, and it frightens us—
We think; but there's a light behind the stars
And we old fellows who have dared to live,
We see it—and we see the other things,
The other things. . . . Yes, I have seen it come   270
These eight years, and these ten years, and I know
Now that it cannot be for very long
That Isaac will be Isaac. You have seen—
Young as you are, you must have seen the strange
Uncomfortable habit of the man?
He'll take my nerves and tie them in a knot
Sometimes, and that's not Isaac. I know that—
And I know what it is: I get it here
A little, in my knees, and Isaac—here."
The old man shook his head regretfully   280
And laid his knuckles three times on his forehead
"That's what it is: Isaac is not quite right.
You see it, but you don't know what it means:
The thousand little differences—no,
You do not know them, and it's well you don't;
You'll know them soon enough—God bless you,
        boy!—
You'll know them, but not all of them—not all.
So think of them as little as you can:
There's nothing in them for you, or for me—

But I am old and I must think of them;   290
I'm in the shadow, but I don't forget
The light, my boy,—the light behind the stars.
Remember that: remember that I said it;
And when the time that you think far away
Shall come for you to say it—say it, boy;
Let there be no confusion or distrust
In you, no snarling of a life half lived,
Nor any cursing over broken things
That your complaint has been the ruin of.
Live to see clearly and the light will come   300
To you, and as you need it.—But there, there,
I'm going it again, as Isaac says,
And I'll stop now before you go to sleep.—
Only be sure that you growl cautiously,
And always where the shadow may not reach you."

Never shall I forget, long as I live,
The quaint thin crack in Archibald's voice,
The lonely twinkle in his little eyes,
Or the way it made me feel to be with him.
I know I lay and looked for a long time   310
Down through the orchard and across the road,
Across the river and the sun-scorched hills
That ceased in a blue forest, where the world
Ceased with it. Now and then my fancy caught
A flying glimpse of a good life beyond—
Something of ships and sunlight, streets and singing,
Troy falling, and the ages coming back,
And ages coming forward: Archibald
And Isaac were good fellows in old clothes,
And Agamemnon was a friend of mine;   320
Ulysses coming home again to shoot
With bows and feathered arrows made another,
And all was as it should be. I was young.

So I lay dreaming of what things I would,
Calm and incorrigibly satisfied
With apples and romance and ignorance,
And the still smoke from Archibald's clay pipe.

There was a stillness over everything,
As if the spirit of heat had laid its hand
Upon the world and hushed it; and I felt   330
Within the mightiness of the white sun
That smote the land around us and wrought out
A fragrance from the trees, a vital warmth
And fullness for the time that was to come,
And a glory for the world beyond the forest.
The present and the future and the past,
Isaac and Archibald, the burning bush,
The Trojans and the walls of Jericho,
Were beautifully fused; and all went well
Till Archibald began to fret for Isaac   340
And said it was a master day for sunstroke.
That was enough to make a mummy smile,
I thought; and I remained hilarious,
In face of all precedence and respect,
Till Isaac (who had come to us unheard)
Found he had no tobacco, looked at me
Peculiarly, and asked of Archibald
What ailed the boy to make him chirrup so.
From that he told us what a blessed world
The Lord had given us.—"But, Archibald,"   350
He added, with a sweet severity
That made me think of peach-skins and goose-flesh.
"I'm half afraid you cut those oats of yours
A day or two before they were well set."
"They were set well enough," said Archibald,—
And I remarked the process of his nose
Before the words came out. "But never mind
Your neighbor's oats: you stay here in the shade
And rest yourself while I go find the cards.
We'll have a little game of seven-up   360
And let the boy keep count."—"We'll have the game,
Assuredly," said Isaac; "and I think
That I will have a drop of cider, also."

They marched away together towards the house
And left me to my childish ruminations

Isaac and Archibald   **154**

Upon the ways of men. I followed them
Down cellar with my fancy, and then left them
For a fairer vision of all things at once
That was anon to be destroyed again
By the sound of voices and of heavy feet—   370
One of the sounds of life that I remember,
Though I forget so many that rang first
As if they were thrown down to me from Sinai.

So I remember, even to this day,
Just how they sounded, how they placed themselves,
And how the game went on while I made marks
And crossed them out, and meanwhile made some
    Trojans.
Likewise I made Ulysses, after Isaac,
And a little after Flaxman. Archibald
Was injured when he found himself left out,   380
But he had no heroics, and I said so:
I told him that his white beard was too long
And too straight down to be like things in Homer.
"Quite so," said Isaac.—"Low," said Archibald;
And he threw down a deuce with a deep grin
That showed his yellow teeth and made me happy.
So they played on till a bell rang from the door,
And Archibald said, "Supper."—After that
The old men smoked while I sat watching them
And wondered with all comfort what might come   390
To me, and what might never come to me;
And when the time came for the long walk home
With Isaac in the twilight, I could see
The forest and the sunset and the sky-line,
No matter where it was that I was looking:
The flame beyond the boundary, the music,
The foam and the white ships, and two old men
Were things that would not leave me.—And that
    night
There came to me a dream—a shining one,
With two old angels in it. They had wings,   400
And they were sitting where a silver light

Suffused them, face to face. The wings of one
Began to palpitate as I approached,
But I was yet unseen when a dry voice
Cried thinly, with unpatronizing triumph,
"I've got you, Isaac; high, low, jack, and the game."

Isaac and Archibald have gone their way
To the silence of the loved and well-forgotten.
I knew them, and I may have laughed at them;
But there's a laughing that has honor in it,   410
And I have no regret for light words now.
Rather I think sometimes they may have made
Their sport of me;—but they would not do that,
They were too old for that. They were old men,
And I may laugh at them because I knew them.

—E. A. ROBINSON

THE RIVER OF LIFE

The more we live, more brief appear
   Our life's succeeding stages:
A day to childhood seems a year,
   And years like passing ages.

The gladsome current of our youth,
   Ere passion yet disorders,
Steals lingering like a river smooth
   Along its grassy borders.

But as the careworn cheek grows wan,
   And sorrow's shafts fly thicker,   10
Ye stars, that measure life to man,
   Why seem your courses quicker?

When joys have lost their bloom and breath,
   And life itself is vapid,

Why, as we reach the falls of death,
    Feel we its tide more rapid?

It may be strange—yet who would change
    Time's course to slower speeding,
When one by one our friends have gone
    And left our bosoms bleeding?   20

Heaven gives our years of fading strength
    Indemnifying fleetness;
And those of youth, a seeming length,
    Proportion'd to their sweetness.
                                —THOMAS CAMPBELL

THE DAY

The day was a year at first
When children ran in the garden;
The day shrank down to a month
When the boys played ball.

The day was a week thereafter
When young men walked in the garden;
The day was itself a day
When love grew tall.

The day shrank down to an hour
When old men limped in the garden;   10
The day will last forever
When it is nothing at all.
                                —THEODORE SPENCER

MORTE D'ARTHUR[1]

So all day long the noise of battle roll'd
Among the mountains by the winter sea,
Until King Arthur's table, man by man,
Had fallen in Lyonesse[2] about their lord,
King Arthur; then, because his wound was deep,
The bold Sir Bedivere uplifted him,
Sir Bedivere, the last of all his knights,
And bore him to a chapel nigh the field,
A broken chancel[3] with a broken cross,
That stood on a dark strait of barren land.   10
On one side lay the ocean, and on one
Lay a great water, and the moon was full.
    Then spake King Arthur to Sir Bedivere:
"The sequel of today unsolders all
The goodliest fellowship of famous knights
Whereof this world holds record. Such a sleep
They sleep—the men I loved. I think that we
Shall never more, at any future time,
Delight our souls with talk of knightly deeds,
Walking about the gardens and the halls   20
Of Camelot,[4] as in the days that were.
I perish by this people which I made,—
Tho' Merlin sware that I should come again
To rule once more—but let what will be, be,
I am so deeply smitten thro' the helm
That without help I cannot last till morn.
Thou therefore take my brand Excalibur,[5]
Which was my pride; for thou rememberest how
In those old days, one summer noon, an arm
Rose up from out the bosom of the lake,   30
Clothed in white samite,[6] mystic, wonderful,
Holding the sword—and how I row'd across
And took it, and have worn it, like a king;
And, wheresoever I am sung or told
In aftertime, this also shall be known.

But now delay not; take Excalibur,
And fling him far into the middle mere;[7]
Watch what thou seest, and lightly bring me word."
    To him replied the bold Sir Bedivere:
"It is not meet,[8] Sir King, to leave thee thus,   40
Aidless, alone, and smitten thro' the helm.
A little thing may harm a wounded man.
Yet I thy hest[9] will all perform at full,
Watch what I see, and lightly bring thee word."
    So saying, from the ruin'd shrine he stept
And in the moon athwart the place of tombs,
Where lay the mighty bones of ancient men,
Old knights, and over them the sea-wind sang
Shrill, chill, with flakes of foam. He, stepping down
By zigzag paths and juts of pointed rock,   50
Came on the shining levels of the lake.
    There drew he forth the brand Excalibur,
And o'er him, drawing it, the winter moon,
Brightening the skirts of a long cloud, ran forth
And sparkled keen with frost against the hilt;
For all the haft twinkled with diamond sparks,
Myriads of topaz-lights, and jacinth[10]-work
Of subtlest jewellery. He gazed so long
That both his eyes were dazzled, as he stood,
This way and that dividing the swift mind,   60
In act to throw; but at the last it seem'd
Better to leave Excalibur conceal'd
There in the many-knotted water-flags,[11]
That whistled stiff and dry about the marge.[12]
So strode he back slow to the wounded king.
    Then spake King Arthur to Sir Bedivere:
"Hast thou perform'd my mission which I gave?
What is it thou hast seen, or what hast heard?"
    And answer made the bold Sir Bedivere:
"I heard the ripple washing in the reeds,   70
And the wild water lapping on the crag."
    To whom replied King Arthur, faint and pale:
"Thou hast betray'd thy nature and thy name,
Not rendering true answer, as beseem'd

Thy fealty, nor like a noble knight;
For surer sign had follow'd, either hand,
Or voice, or else a motion of the mere,
This is a shameful thing for men to lie.
Yet now, I charge thee, quickly go again
As thou art lief[13] and dear, and do the thing   80
I bade thee, watch, and lightly bring me word."
    Then went Sir Bedivere the second time
Across the ridge, and paced beside the mere,
Counting the dewy pebbles, fix'd in thought;
But when he saw the wonder of the hilt,
How curiously and strangely chased, he smote
His palms together, and he cried aloud:
    "And if indeed I cast the brand away,
Surely a precious thing, one worthy note,
Should thus be lost forever from the earth,   90
Which might have pleased the eyes of many men.
What good should follow this, if this were done?
What harm, undone? deep harm to disobey,
Seeing obedience is the bond of rule.
Were it well to obey then, if a king demand
An act unprofitable, against himself?
The king is sick, and knows not what he does.
What record, or what relic of my lord
Should be to aftertime, but empty breath
And rumours of a doubt? but were this kept,   100
Stored in some treasure-house of mighty kings.
Some one might show it at a joust of arms,
Saying, 'King Arthur's sword, Excalibur,
Wrought by the lonely maiden of the lake;
Nine years she wrought it, sitting in the deeps
Upon the hidden bases of the hills.'
So might some old man speak in the aftertime
To all the people, winning reverence;
But now much honour and much fame were lost."
    So spake he, clouded with his own conceit,[14]   110
And hid Excalibur the second time,
And so strode back slow to the wounded king.
    Then spoke King Arthur, breathing heavily:

Morte D'Arthur   **160**

"What is it thou hast seen, or what hast heard?"
   And answer made the bold Sir Bedivere:
"I heard the water lapping on the crag,
And the long ripple washing in the reeds."
   To whom replied King Arthur, much in wrath:
"Ah, miserable and unkind, untrue,
Unknightly, traitor-hearted! Woe is me!   120
Authority forgets a dying king,
Laid widow'd of the power in his eye
That bow'd the will. I see thee what thou art,
For thou, the latest-left of all my knights,
In whom should meet the offices of all,
Thou wouldst betray me for the precious hilt;
Either from lust of gold, or like a girl
Valuing the giddy pleasure of the eyes.
Yet, for a man may fail in duty twice,
And the third time may prosper, get thee hence;   130
But, if thou spare to fling Excalibur,
I will arise and slay thee with my hands."
   Then quickly rose Sir Bedivere, and ran,
And, leaping down the ridges lightly, plunged
Among the bulrush-beds, and clutch'd the sword,
And strongly wheel'd and threw it. The great brand
Made lightnings in the splendour of the moon,
And flashing round and round, and whirl'd in an arch,
Shot like a streamer of the northern morn,[15]
Seen where the moving isles of winter[16] shock   140
By night, with noises of the northern sea.
So flash'd and fell the brand Excalibur:
But ere he dipt the surface, rose an arm
Cloth'd in white samite, mystic, wonderful,
And caught him by the hilt, and brandish'd him
Three times, and drew him under in the mere.
And lightly went the other to the King.
   Then spoke King Arthur, drawing thicker breath:
"Now see I by thine eyes that this is done.
Speak out: what is it thou hast heard or seen?"   150
   And answer made the bold Sir Bedivere:
"Sir King, I closed mine eyelids, lest the gems

Morte D'Arthur   **161**

Should blind my purpose, for I never saw,
Nor shall see, here or elsewhere, till I die,
Not tho' I live three lives of mortal men,
So great a miracle as yonder hilt.
Then with both hands I flung him, wheeling him;
But when I look'd again, behold an arm,
Clothed in white samite, mystic, wonderful,
That caught him by the hilt, and brandish'd him   160
Three times, and drew him under in the mere."
    And answer made King Arthur, breathing hard:
"My end draws nigh; 'tis time that I were gone.
Make broad thy shoulders to receive my weight,
And bear me to the margin; yet I fear
My wound hath taken cold, and I shall die."
    So saying, from the pavement he half rose,
Slowly, with pain, reclining on his arm,
And looking wistfully with wide blue eyes
As in a picture. Him Sir Bedivere   170
Remorsefully regarded thro' his tears,
And would have spoken, but he found not words,
Then took with care, and kneeling on one knee,
O'er both his shoulders drew the languid hands.
And rising bore him thro' the place of tombs.
    But, as he walk'd, King Arthur panted hard,
Like one that feels a nightmare on his bed
When all the house is mute. So sigh'd the King,
Muttering and murmuring at his ear, "Quick, quick!
I fear it is too late, and I shall die."   180
But the other swiftly strode from ridge to ridge,
Clothed with his breath, and looking, as he walk'd,
Larger than human on the frozen hills.
He heard the deep behind him, and a cry
Before. His own thought drove him like a goad.
Dry clash'd his harness in the icy caves
And barren chasms, and all to left and right
The bare black cliff clang'd round him, as he based
His feet on juts of slippery crag that rang
Sharp-smitten with the dint of armed heels—   190
And on a sudden, lo! the level lake,

Morte D'Arthur   **162**

And the long glories of the winter moon.
Then saw they how there hove a dusky barge
Dark as a funeral scarf from stem to stern,
Beneath them; and descending they were ware
That all the decks were dense with stately forms
Black-stoled, black-hooded, like a dream—by these
Three Queens with crowns of gold—and from them
     rose
A cry that shiver'd to the tingling stars,
And, as it were one voice, an agony   200
Of lamentation, like a wind, that shrills
All night in a waste land, where no one comes,
Or hath come, since the making of the world.
   Then murmur'd Arthur, "Place me in the barge,"
And to the barge they came. There those three Queens
Put forth their hands, and took the King, and wept.
But she that rose the tallest of them all
And fairest, laid his head upon her lap.
And loosed the shatter'd casque, and chafed his
     hands,
And call'd him by his name, complaining loud,   210
And dropping bitter tears against his brow
Striped with dark blood: for all his face was white
And colourless, and like the wither'd moon
Smote by the fresh beam of the springing east;
And all his greaves and cuisses[17] dash'd with drops
Of onset;[18] and the light and lustrous curls—
That made his forehead like a rising sun
High from the dais-throne—were parch'd with dust
Or, clotted into points and hanging loose,
Mix'd with the knightly growth that fringed his lips.   220
So like a shatter'd column lay the King;
Not like that Arthur who, with lance in rest,
From spur to plume a star of tournament,
Shot thro' the lists at Camelot, and charged
Before the eyes of ladies and of kings.
   Then loudly cried the bold Sir Bedivere,
"Ah! my Lord Arthur, whither shall I go?
Where shall I hide my forehead and my eyes?

Morte D'Arthur   **163**

For now I see the true old times are dead,
When every morning brought a noble chance,   230
And every chance brought out a noble knight.
Such times have been not since the light hath led [19]
The holy Elders with the gift of myrrh.
But now the whole ROUND TABLE is dissolved
Which was an image of the mighty world;
And I, the last, go forth companionless,
And the days darken round me, and the years,
Among new men, strange faces, other minds."
    And slowly answer'd Arthur from the barge:
"The old order changeth, yielding place to new,   240
And God fulfils himself in many ways,
Lest one good custom should corrupt the world.
Comfort thyself: what comfort is in me?
I have lived my life, and that which I have done
May He within himself make pure! but thou,
If thou shouldst never see my face again,
Pray for my soul. More things are wrought by prayer
Than this world dreams of. Wherefore, let thy voice
Rise like a fountain for me night and day.
For what are men better than sheep or goats   250
That nourish a blind life within the brain,
If, knowing God, they lift not hands of prayer
Both for themselves and those who call them friend?
For so the whole round earth is every way
Bound by gold chains about the feet of God.
But now farewell. I am going a long way
With these thou seest—if indeed I go—
For all my mind is clouded with a doubt—
To the island-valley of Avilion;[20]
Where falls not hail, or rain, or any snow,   260
Nor ever wind blows loudly, but it lies
Deep-meadow'd, happy, fair with orchard lawns
And bowery hollows crown'd with summer sea,
Where I will heal me of my grievous wound."
    So said he, and the barge with oar and sail
Moved from the brink, like some full-breasted swan
That, fluting a wild carol ere her death,

Ruffles her pure cold plume, and takes the flood
With swarthy webs. Long stood Sir Bedivere
Revolving many memories, till the hull   270
Look'd one black dot against the verge of dawn,
And on the mere the wailing died away.
                        —ALFRED LORD TENNYSON

BY THE STATUE OF
KING CHARLES AT CHARING CROSS

Somber and rich, the skies;
Great glooms, and starry plains.
Gently the night wind sighs;
Else a vast silence reigns.

The splendid silence clings
Around me; and around
The saddest of all kings
Crowned, and again discrowned.

Comely and calm, he rides
Hard by his own Whitehall.   10
Only the night wind glides;
No crowds, nor rebels, brawl.

Gone too, his court; and yet,
The stars his courtiers are—
Stars in their stations set,
And every wandering star.

Alone he rides, alone,
The fair and fatal king;
Dark night is all his own,
That strange and solemn thing.   20

Which are more full of fate—
The stars, or those sad eyes?
Which are more still and great—

Those brows, or the skies?

Although his whole heart yearn
In passionate tragedy,
Never was face so stern
With sweet austerity.

Vanquished in life, his death
By beauty made amends;   30
The passing of his breath
Won his defeated ends.[1]

Brief life, and hapless? Nay;
Through death, life grew sublime.
Speak after sentence? [2] Yea—
And to the end of time.

Armored he rides, his head
Bare to the stars of doom;
He triumphs now, the dead,
Beholding London's gloom.   40

Our wearier spirit faints,
Vexed in the world's employ;
His soul was of the saints,
And art to him was joy.[3]

King, tried in fires of woe!
Men hunger for thy grace;
And through the night I go,
Loving thy mournful face.

Yet, when the city sleeps,
When all the cries are still,   50
The stars and heavenly deeps
Work out a perfect will.

—LIONEL JOHNSON

section eleven.

The contradictory character of man is the
theme of three poems. Then Sir Henry Wotton
writes about one kind of happy life.

THE GULL

Riding the wind, in planetary sweep
The gull wheels on the radius of a wing;
Ocean and air, concourse of height and deep,
Acclaim the exultant orbit of their king.

Precise he lands, defter than any dancer,
Red legs, red eye, white body, whiter than foam;
No loveliest yacht so light to lean and answer,
No soul so white in its celestial home.

O Attic joy, O grace made visible,
Beauty and joy embodied into bird!   10
Malice, or truth—which is it pricks your spell
With sarcasm of the loathsome and absurd?

Those lacquered feathers, sleek to wind and wave,
Or downy to the softly-fingering breeze,
Are an infested jungle, a living grave,
The haunt of lice, mites, parasites, and fleas.

Filth feeds that savage beauty; when head, beak, eyes
Plunge in the putrid whale, or, harsh as sin,
Are stretched agape, with cannibalistic cries,
To tear the wounded body of his kin.   20

The Gull   **167**

O beauty born of death, to death returning,
You are our Middle Earth, nor Heaven nor Hell;
You are ourselves, our turning globe still turning,
The fractured light in which we have to dwell.

Here truth is ever tangent. Therefore, gull,
Gorged with the stinking offal that you eat,
Rise in the light, infested, beautiful,
In fragmentary loveliness complete.

—MICHAEL THWAITES

MAN

I know my body's of so frail a kind,
    As force without, fevers within, can kill;
I know the heavenly nature of my mind,
    But 'tis corrupted both in wit and will.

I know my soul hath power to know all things
    Yet is she blind and ignorant in all;
I know I am one of nature's little kings,
    Yet to the least and vilest things am thrall.

I know my life's a pain, and but a span;
    I know my sense is mocked with everything;   10
And to conclude, I know myself a man,
    Which is a proud, and yet a wretched thing.

—SIR JOHN DAVIES

RIDDLE OF THE WORLD

Know then thyself, presume not God to scan,
The proper study of Mankind is Man.
Plac'd on this isthmus of a middle state,
A Being darkly wise, and rudely great:
With too much knowledge for the Sceptic side,
With too much weakness for the Stoic's pride,

He hangs between; in doubt to act, or rest;
In doubt to deem himself a God, or Beast;
In doubt his Mind or Body to prefer;
Born but to die, and reas'ning but to err;   10
Alike in ignorance, his reason such,
Whether he thinks too little, or too much:
Chaos of Thought and Passion, all confus'd;
Still by himself abus'd, or disabus'd;
Created half to rise, and half to fall;
Great Lord of all things, yet a prey to all;
Sole judge of truth, in endless error hurl'd:
The glory, jest, and riddle of the world!

—ALEXANDER POPE

CHARACTER OF A HAPPY LIFE

How happy is he born and taught
   That serveth not another's will;
Whose armor is his honest thought
   And simple truth his utmost skill!

Whose passions not his masters are,
   Whose soul is still prepared for death,
Not tied unto the world with care
   Of public fame, or private breath;

Who envies none that chance doth raise,
   Or vice; Who never understood   10
How deepest wounds are given by praise;
   Nor rules of state, but rules of good:

Who hath his life from rumors freed,
   Whose conscience is his strong retreat;
Whose state can neither flatterers feed,
   Nor ruin make accusers great;

Who God doth late and early pray
   More of his grace than gifts to lend;

And entertains the harmless day
   With a well-chosen book or friend;

—This man is freed from servile bands
   Of hope to rise, or fear to fall;
Lord of himself, though not of lands,
   And having nothing, yet hath all.
                              —SIR HENRY WOTTON

section twelve.

Two poets speculate beyond.

REQUIEM

Will they stop,
Will they stand there for a moment, perhaps before
 some shop where you have gone so many times
(Stand with the same blue sky above them and the
 stones, so often walked, beneath)

Will it be a day like this—
As though there could be such a day again—
And will their own concerns still be about the same,
And will the feeling still be this that you have felt so
 many times,
Will they meet and stop and speak, one perplexed
 and one aloof,

Saying: Have you heard,
Have you heard,   10
Have you heard about the death?

Yes, choosing the words, tragic, yes, a shock,
One who had so much of this, they will say, a life so
 filled with that,
Then will one say that the days are growing crisp
 again, the other that the leaves are turning,
And will they say good-bye, good-bye, you must look
 me up some time, good-bye,
Then turn and go, each of them thinking, and yet,
 and yet,

Requiem   **171**

Each feeling, if it were I, instead, would that be all,
Each wondering, suddenly alone, if that is all, in
fact—

And will that be all?
On a day like this, with motors streaming through the
fresh parks, the streets alive with casual people,   20
And everywhere, on all of it, the brightness of the
sun.

—KENNETH FEARING

AFTERWARDS

When the Present has latched its postern[1] behind my
tremulous stay,
And the May month flaps its glad green leaves like
wings,
Delicate-filmed as new-spun silk, will the neigh-
bours say,
  "He was a man who used to notice such things"?

If it be in the dusk when, like an eyelid's soundless
blink,
The dewfall-hawk comes crossing the shades to alight
Upon the wind-warped upland thorn, a gazer may
think,
  "To him this must have been a familiar sight."

If I pass during some nocturnal blackness, mothy
and warm,
When the hedgehog travels furtively over the lawn,   10
One may say, "He strove that such innocent creatures
should come to no harm,
But he could do little for them; and now he is gone."

If, when hearing that I have been stilled at last, they
stand at the door,
Watching the full-starred heavens that winter sees,

Will this thought rise on those who will meet my
    face no more,
  "He was one who had an eye for such mysteries"?

And will any say when my bell of quittance^2 is heard
    in the gloom,
And a crossing breeze cuts a pause in its outrollings,
Till they rise again, as they were a new bell's boom,
  "He hears it not now, but used to notice such
    things"?

—THOMAS HARDY

notes to the poems

1. *Ithaka* (usually spelled "Ithaca"): the kingdom of Ulysses (Odysseus), an island off the west coast of Greece. Ulysses, one of the Greek leaders in the war against Troy, did not return to Ithaca and his wife Penelope until after an absence of 20 years. His fabulous journey home is narrated in Homer's epic, *The Odyssey*.
2. *Laistrygonians:* a savage race of cannibals whom Odysseus (Ulysses) encountered in his wanderings.
3. *Cyclops:* Polyphemus, a son of Poseidon, was one of the Cyclops. Odysseus blinded this gigantic monster, who had only one eye in the center of his forehead. By doing so, Odysseus incurred the wrath of Poseidon.

ULYSSES

1. This poem, written by Tennyson in 1833 in the midst of his grief for his dead friend, Arthur Hallam, is one of the great examples in literature of what might be called *transference*. In this process an emotion aroused by a specific set of circumstances is expressed through an altogether different set. The poem embodied, Tennyson said, "my feeling about the need of going forward, and braving the struggle of life. . . ." The suggestion for this last voyage of Ulysses came from Homer (*Odyssey* XI. 100–37) and from Dante (the 26th Canto of the *Inferno*).
2. *rainy Hyades:* The rainy season began, it was thought, when the Hyades, a group of five stars in the head of

the constellation Taurus, rose at the same time as the sun.

3. *Happy Isles:* the Elysian Fields, the Greek paradise for virtuous men after death.

ON FIRST LOOKING INTO CHAPMAN'S HOMER

1. *Which bards . . . hold:* Which poets hold by oath of fidelity to Apollo, the god of music and poetry.
2. *demesne:* domain.
3. *Chapman:* George Chapman (1559?–1634), Elizabethan playwright, poet, and translator.
4. *Cortez:* actually Balboa.

A MISSOURI TRAVELLER WRITES HOME: 1830

1. *Judith, Larb, Crazy Hills:* all areas north of the Missouri River that provide streams tributary to it.
2. *Medusa's head,* covered with snakes instead of hair, was so fearful that anyone looking at it was turned to stone.
3. *white bear:* not, obviously, the polar bear, but probably a light-colored grizzly.

ROMANCE

1. The three places mentioned in this poem are all very high mountains, Popocatapetl in Mexico, the other two in Equador. They are probably to be associated with the remote and exotic, and more particularly with the romance of the Spanish Conquest.

DAYS

1. *dervishes:* Moslem monks or friars.
2. *pleached garden:* a garden covered by interlaced vines. The reference probably is meant to strike the note of formality and the artificial.

MY LAST DUCHESS

1. *Fra:* Brother; Pandolfo was a monk.

THE HAYSTACK IN THE FLOODS

1. Sir Robert de Marny, an English knight who fought at Poictiers (1356), is riding through France with Jehane, his mistress, and a small company. They are confronted by Godmar (a renegade Englishman?), who has been waiting to waylay Robert and carry off Jehane.
2. *kirtle kilted:* skirt tucked up.
3. *coif:* a close-fitting cap, similar to a hood. Jehane tried to pull it over her eyes so that she might not see Robert slain.
4. *Gascon frontier:* Gascony, in southwestern France, was English territory at the time.
5. *those six men:* the judges who would try her as a witch, meanwhile imprisoning her in the Grand Chatelet, a Paris prison.
6. *St. George:* patron saint of the English.
7. *fitte:* a division of a poem, song, or story.

THE REVENGE OF HAMISH

1. *ten-tined:* ten-pointed (antlers).
2. *bracken:* large, coarse ferns.
3. *burn:* brook.
4. *bating:* abating or lessening.
5. *kern:* peasant.
6. *gillie:* servant.
7. *bairn:* baby.

THE RIME OF THE ANCIENT MARINER

1. Readers interested in the background and "meaning" of Coleridge's great poem are referred to Chapter XIV of the poet's *Biographia Literaria,* to John Livingston Lowe's *Road to Xanadu,* and, for a review of interpretations subsequent to, and possibly superseding, Lowe's, to Frederick A. Pottle, "Teaching the Poem:

The Ancient Mariner," *Reports and Speeches of the Fourth Yale Conference on the Teaching of English* (M.A.T. Program, Yale University, 1958).

2. *eftsoons:* immediately.
3. *kirk:* church (Scottish).
4. *minstrelsy:* musicians.
5. *clifts:* cliffs.
6. *ken:* see.
7. *swound:* swoon (faint).
8. *vespers nine:* nine evenings.
9. *reel and rout:* dance and uproar.
10. *death-fires:* luminous appearances above dead bodies.
11. *wist:* know.
12. *As:* As if.
13. *work us weal:* do us good (compare "work 'em woe," line 92).
14. *clomb:* climbed.
15. *fire-flags sheen:* bright lightning flashes.
16. *jag:* fork.
17. *corses:* corpses.
18. *jargoning:* warbling, twittering.
19. *have not to declare:* cannot say.
20. *charnel:* burial.
21. *rood:* cross.
22. *shrieve:* hear confession and give absolution.
23. *ivy-tod:* ivy bush.
24. *forlorn:* deprived.

THE DESTRUCTION OF SENNACHERIB

1. *Sennacherib* was a king of Assyria who invaded Palestine in the seventh century B.C. The Biblical source of the poem is II Kings 18, 19.
2. *Ashur:* the highest god of the Assyrians.
3. *Baal:* the supreme deity of the Canaanites and the Phoenicians.

WHEN, IN DISGRACE WITH FORTUNE AND MEN'S EYES
1. *bootless:* profitless.

MAID OF ATHENS, ERE WE PART

1. The Greek refrain is pronounced "Zō-ay moo sahss agapó," and means "My life, I love thee."

LA BELLE DAME SANS MERCI

1. *sedge:* grasslike plants growing in marshy places.
2. *meads:* meadows.
3. *zone:* belt or girdle.
4. *grot:* grotto or cave.
5. *thrall:* slavery.

SEE WHERE CAPELLA

1. *Capella:* a large star in the constellation Auriga; one of the brightest stars in the heavens. The Greeks thought of it as representing a she-goat; its attendant stars are known as the Haedi, or Kids.

VAE VICTIS

1. *Scythians:* in classical times, a term applied to various savage, nomadic peoples.

POLO GROUNDS

1. The time is the '30s; the home team is the New York Giants, later to move to San Francisco; and the visitors, the Brooklyn Dodgers, later to move to Los Angeles.

SHALL I COMPARE THEE TO A SUMMER'S DAY?

1. *lease:* term (as of a lease).
2. *every fair from fair:* every beautiful thing (or woman) from beauty.
3. *untrimm'd:* stripped of beauty.
4. *thou ow'st:* you own.

THE STATUE

1. *Syracusan:* Syracuse was, in classical times, the wealthiest and most populous town in Sicily.
2. *Praxiteles:* with Phidias, the greatest of Greek sculptors. His *Hermes* appears to be the only statue extant that can be reasonably well proven to be an original.

THE CHOICE

1. Whether these three incidents—all examples of courage in the face of death, and the last two evidently drawn from World War II—are historical is, according to Mr. Corke, irrelevant.

THE LAND

1. *dreenin':* draining.
2. *wains:* wagons.
3. *flitches:* slices, portions, parts.
4. *sile:* soil.
5. *spile:* buttress (in this case, the banks of a stream) by driving in piles.
6. *Georgii Quinti,* etc.: in the sixth year of the reign of George V, which began in 1910.
7. *rights of chase and warren:* the right to hunt, and to keep in a guarded place certain animals.
8. *tickles:* catches fish (usually trout) by rubbing them on the belly.
9. *wires:* catches animals or birds by trapping with wire snares.
10. *swapped a hedge:* cut the hedge down, presumably to provide access to certain territory.
11. *faggot:* a small piece of firewood.
12. *conies:* rabbits.
13. *Pan:* the god of nature.
14. *Domesday Book:* an inventory of people and property drawn up at the command of William the Conqueror upon his seizure of England in 1066.
15. *Mus':* dialect form of "Mister."

1. *sea-gate, dyke, and groin:* all protective devices against the encroachments of the sea: the first, a gate closed at high tide; the second, a wall constructed to hold off the sea; the third, a jetty placed to divert the force of the waves.
2. *saltings:* land covered by the sea at high tide.
3. *sluices:* adjustable gates for letting water in or out.
4. *bents:* stiff, coarse grass.
5. *furze:* a spiny evergreen shrub.
6. *hurdles:* a movable frame for enclosing land.
7. *tow:* coarse flax or hemp used for tinder.

MR. FLOOD'S PARTY

1. *Roland's ghost . . . horn:* Roland, the most famous of Charlemagne's knights, blew his horn in a vain appeal for help at Roncesvalles, and was slain.

ISAAC AND ARCHIBALD

1. *Flaxman:* English sculptor and draughtsman (1755–1826), famed, among other accomplishments, for his engravings of Homeric characters.

MORTE D'ARTHUR

1. This poem, published in 1842, later became the twelfth book of the *Idylls of the King*.
2. *Lyonesse:* a legendary land west of Cornwall, England, said since to have sunk beneath the sea.
3. *chancel:* the part of a church east of the nave, including the altar, pulpit, and lectern, and occupied by the clergy and usually the choir.
4. *Camelot:* King Arthur's capital.
5. *brand Excalibur:* King Arthur's sword, given him by the Lady of the Lake.
6. *samite:* a heavy silk interwoven with gold and silver threads.

7. *into the middle mere:* into the pool or lake, the "great water" mentioned in line 12.
8. *meet:* fitting.
9. *hest:* command.
10. *jacinth:* hyacinth, a gem of the ancients.
11. *water-flags:* water-irises.
12. *marge:* shore.
13. *lief:* beloved.
14. *conceit:* conception, thought.
15. *streamer of the northern morn:* the Aurora Borealis.
16. *moving isles of winter:* icebergs.
17. *greaves and cuisses:* armor for the shins and thighs.
18. *drops of onset:* blood from battle-wounds.
19. *light hath led:* the star of Bethlehem.
20. *Avilion:* (or Avalon), the Isle of Souls or Land of the Blessed in Arthurian legend.

BY THE STATUE OF KING CHARLES AT CHARING CROSS

1. *passing . . . end:* The dignity and patience with which Charles met his end so stirred the people that the power of Parliament was shaken.
2. *Speak after sentence?:* After Charles was sentenced, he asked permission to speak, a request refused by the court.
3. *art . . . joy:* In his palaces in Whitehall and Richmond, Charles made one of the finest collections of paintings in Europe.

AFTERWARDS

1. *postern:* a back door or gate.
2. *bell of quittance:* a bell rung as part of the ritual of a funeral procession.

biographical notes

AUDEN, W. H. (1907――) is one of the most distinguished, and certainly the most versatile, of modern poets. Born in York and educated at Oxford, he emigrated to the United States in 1939, and is now an American citizen. A poet must be, he has said, "a person passionately in love with language." He won the Pulitzer Prize in 1948 for his long poem, *The Age of Anxiety*.

BLY, ROBERT (1926――) lives in Madison, Minnesota, where he edits *The Sixties*, a literary magazine. Besides writing poetry, he is a translator.

BRIDGES, ROBERT (1844–1930) was Poet Laureate from 1913 until his death. What was to be his enduring monument—*The Testament of Beauty* (1929)—is now unread; but his name may stay alive through a few shorter poems and through his unselfish encouragement of a greater poet, Gerard Manley Hopkins.

BROWNING, ROBERT (1812–89) created the dramatic monologue, of which "My Last Duchess" is perhaps the best-known example. He and Tennyson are the giants of Victorian poetry. Browning is almost equally famous as a husband; *The Barretts of Wimpole Street* records in dramatic form his courtship of Elizabeth Barrett.

BYRON, GEORGE GORDON, LORD (1788–1824) was, during his lifetime, notorious in England for his unconventional behavior, famous in Greece for his involvement in the War for Independence. As a poet he is honored for his satires, his romantic lyrics, and his stirring narratives.

CAMPBELL, ROY (1901–57) was one of the few poets to have come out of the Union of South Africa, where he lived until 1926, when he emigrated to England.

CAMPBELL, THOMAS (1777–1844). This Scottish poet is best known for his stirring war poems, "Hohenlinden," "The Battle of the Baltic," and "Ye Mariners of England."

CAVAFY (1863–1933), the most famous of modern Greek poets, lived most of his life in Alexandria, where, according to E. M. Forster, he appeared in the streets as "a Greek gentleman, in a straw hat, standing absolutely motionless at a slight angle to the universe." "Ithaka" is a highly popular poem among young people in Greece today.

COLERIDGE, SAMUEL TAYLOR (1772–1834). "The Ancient Mariner," "Christabel," and "Kubla Khan" are the most important poems of this English poet, critic, philosopher, conversationalist, and close friend of another great poet, William Wordsworth.

CORKE, HILARY (1921——). When asked for information about himself, Mr. Corke proposed the following:

Hilary Corke was born in 1921 of correctly assorted parents, head foremost. After being confined for a number of years in institutions, he was sentenced in 1940, on account of a major crime of which he still protests his complete innocence, to five years' penal servitude. Upon his final release in 1948, he obtained by means of false representations a post as assistant warder in an Egyptian prison; and a similar one, using this time a forged letter of reference, in a Scottish prison in 1952. By 1956 he had amassed sufficient capital to enable him to set up a full-time criminal organization. He is understood to be now operating from a rural hideout, and to have been the brains behind a number of the most unspectacular crimes of recent years.

He then appended a "polite version":

Born 1921, in Malvern, Worcestershire, England.

Educated Charterhouse and Christ Church, Oxford. Served in Royal Artillery (Captain) 1940–45. Lecturer in Medieval English at the University of Cairo, Egypt, 1948; and in that of Edinburgh, Scotland, 1952. Since 1956 a free-lance writer, contributing poems, short stories, essays, and reviews to most of the leading periodicals on both sides of the Atlantic. *The Early Drowned* (poems), Secker & Warburg, London, 1961. Married, and lives in Surrey, England, with his wife and four small children.

COWLEY, MALCOLM (1898 ——) is best known as a literary critic and as the historian of the expatriate *(Exile's Return)*. "The Long Voyage" is from his book of poetry, *The Dry Season* (1941). He lives in Sherman, Connecticut.

DAVIES, SIR JOHN (1569–1626) was solicitor general and attorney general for Ireland in the reign of Charles I, and a philosopher and poet. "Man," excerpted from a larger work, is his one piece of writing that has survived.

DE LA MARE, WALTER (1873–1956) was a compiler of highly original anthologies—*Come Hither* (poetry) and *Behold, This Dreamer* (dream literature); a novelist *(Memoirs of a Midget);* and a great and prolific poet.

EASTMAN, MAX (1883——) has been a literary and social critic and student of Marxism, as well as poet. He founded and edited the liberal periodicals, *The Masses* and *The Liberator*.

EMERSON, RALPH WALDO (1803–82), resident of Concord, Massachusetts, was a friend of Thoreau, Alcott, Margaret Fuller, and Hawthorne; leader of the philosophical movement of Transcendentalism; essayist ("Self-Reliance," "Compensation," "The Over-Soul"); and poet.

FEARING, KENNETH (1902–61), American poet, was noted for the unconventionality of his techniques and for his satiric attitude toward modern life; he also wrote novels of suspense—*The Hospital, The Big Clock*.

FRANCIS, ROBERT (1901——). *The Orb Weaver* (1960),

from which "Pitcher" is taken, is the latest of the five books of poetry by this poet and teacher, who lives in a one-room house in Amherst, Massachusetts.

FROST, ROBERT (1874–1963) was the dominant figure in American poetry during the first half of this century.

HALL, DONALD (1928———) was graduated from Phillips Exeter Academy and Harvard University, and attended Oxford, where he won the Newdigate Prize. He is editor of poetry anthologies as well as poet. He is now teaching at the University of Michigan.

HARDY, THOMAS (1840–1928) was best known in his lifetime for his novels, but his poetry may ultimately bring him greater fame.

HOLMES, JOHN (1904–62) was a poet and critic of poetry, and for many years Professor of English at Tufts University. "The Somerset Dam for Supper" is from his last book of poetry, *The Fortune Teller*.

HOUSMAN, A. E. (1859–1936) is immortalized in three books of verse—*The Shropshire Lad* (1896), *Last Poems* (1922), and *More Poems* (posthumously published, 1936). He was also a distinguished scholar of Latin literature.

HUMPHRIES, ROLFE (1894———), American poet, has been a secondary-school teacher of Latin, a translator of Virgil and Ovid, and, since 1957, Lecturer in English at Amherst College.

JEFFERS, ROBINSON (1887–1962). "Cut humanity out of my being, that is the wound that festers." He celebrated the natural world because it was beautiful and because it was nonhuman. He made famous the California coast of Carmel and Point Sur.

JOHNSON, LIONEL (1867–1902) was a scholar-poet and critic, a convert to Catholicism, and a lover of the Celtic. He was an intimate friend of W. B. Yeats.

KEATS, JOHN (1795–1821). Along with Wordsworth and Coleridge, his older contemporaries, and Byron and Shelley, who, like him, died young, he shared in that concatenation of impulses and ideas now known as the Romantic Movement. His sonnets, his odes, his "Eve of Saint Agnes" made him one of the great figures of English literature.

KIPLING, RUDYARD (1865–1936). Born in Bombay, he became the great poet and prose-writer of British India and *the* apologist for Imperialism. "Cities and Thrones and Powers" reveals the more sensitive side of this celebrator of the everyday world, this creator of heroic rhythms.

LANIER, SIDNEY (1842–81). This Southern musician, literary critic, and poet has survived in a few poems, among which "Song of the Chattahoochee" is the best known.

LAWRENCE, D. H. (1885–1930). This son of a Derbyshire miner became one of the century's most controversial literary figures. As novelist, writer of short stories, and poet, he acclaimed the sexual instinct and "natural behavior," and inveighed against "intellectualism."

LINDSAY, VACHEL (1879–1931). Like Carl Sandburg, he brought poetry from the printed page to the concert hall. Self-consciously bardic, he tramped America preaching his gospel of beauty. His best known poem is "The Congo."

LOWELL, AMY (1874–1925), American poet, was a leader of the Imagist movement, which emphasized the language of common speech, precision and hard clarity of image, and the creation of new rhythms. She won the Pulitzer Prize, awarded her posthumously in 1926, for *What's O'clock?*

MACLEISH, ARCHIBALD (1892——) gave up law for poetry, and has also been a college professor and Librarian of Congress. His *Conquistador,* a saga-poem on the Spanish conquest of Mexico, won the Pulitzer Prize in 1933.

MARKHAM, EDWIN (1852–1940) was a teacher and school superintendent in his native California until "The Man with the Hoe" made him famous in 1899. He wrote

"Lincoln, the Man of the People" in 1922 for the dedication of the Lincoln Memorial.

MATCHETT, WILLIAM H. (1923——) has produced one volume of poetry, the title-poem of which is in this anthology. Once assistant to Archibald MacLeish in his poetry course at Harvard, he now teaches English at the University of Washington.

MCKELLAR, J. A. R. (1904–32). His death at twenty-seven silenced a voice that might have contributed much to Australia's search for a non-colonial literature. A selection of his verse can be found in *The Penguin Book of Australian Poetry*.

MILLAY, EDNA ST. VINCENT (1892–1950). No American poet has displayed more skill in the sonnet form; it now seems probable that this literary idol of the 'twenties and 'thirties will live on for this achievement.

MORRIS, WILLIAM (1834–96), English poet, was also distinguished as artist and decorator, manufacturer of textiles and furniture (the Morris chair), printer, and socialist.

MUIR, JOHN (1838–1914) was a Scottish-American naturalist whose passion for the study of nature took him to every part of the world. Among his major works are *The Mountains of California* (1894), *My First Summer in the Sierra* (1911) and *The Yosemite* (1912).

NEMEROV, HOWARD (1920——) has published, besides considerable literary criticism, three novels, a book of short stories, and five books of poetry. He teaches at Bennington College.

OWEN, WILFRED (1893–1918) died in battle a week before the Armistice. His verse became famous when his friend Siegfried Sassoon put together a posthumous collection. Owen had written: ". . . this book is not concerned with Poetry,/ The subject of it is War, and the pity of War./ The Poetry is in the pity."

POPE, ALEXANDER (1688–1744), satiric and philosophical poet, and translator of Homer, was the dominant literary figure of the first half of the eighteenth century.

ROBINSON, EDWIN ARLINGTON (1869–1935) is by many considered to be, along with Frost, the most distinguished of twentieth-century American poets. He was thrice winner of the Pulitzer Prize. He is perhaps best known for his psychological portraits of New England small-town people (Robinson came from Gardiner, Maine).

SASSOON, SIEGFRIED (1886——). His three books of poems—*The Old Huntsman* (1917), *Counter-Attack* (1918), *Picture Show* (1920)—are unsparing revelations of the horrors of modern war.

SHAKESPEARE, WILLIAM (1564–1616). Shakespeare the playwright was also Shakespeare the sonneteer. Two of his sonnets are in this anthology.

SHIRLEY, JAMES (1596–1666) belongs to the generation of poets and dramatists who succeeded Shakespeare. "Death the Leveller" is his best-known poem.

SPENCER, THEODORE (1902–49) was widely known as a Shakespearean scholar and literary critic before he published his first book of poetry in 1941. Three more books followed before his death at the age of forty-six.

STEPHENS, JAMES (1882–1950) was a lover of Ireland and recreator of Irish folklore and fairy tales, and a sympathizer with the frail, the small, the downtrodden.

TENNYSON, ALFRED, LORD (1809–92) was Poet Laureate of England from 1850 till his death, and author of "In Memoriam," *Idylls of the King,* "Locksley Hall," "The Charge of the Light Brigade" and many other famous poems.

THOMAS, EDWARD (1878–1917) died in World War I. He was an essayist, biographer, and critic as well as poet, and an intimate of Robert Frost during the latter's sojourn in England.

THWAITES, MICHAEL (1915——) is a native of Australia. Like Donald Hall, he has won the Newdigate Prize at Oxford. During World War II he commanded a corvette. Upon returning to Australia he became a civil servant. He has published one book of poetry.

TURNER, W. J. (1889–1946). "Romance" is the best-remembered poem of this Australian-born poet, who was also a London drama and music critic.

UPDIKE, JOHN (1932——) is the author of three novels—*The Poorhouse Fair, Rabbit Run,* and *The Centaur;* of two collections of short stories—*The Same Door* and *Pigeon Feathers;* and of two books of poetry—*The Carpentered Hen* and *Telephone Poles.*

WHITMAN, WALT (1819–92). Upon the publication of *Leaves of Grass* in 1855, Emerson wrote Whitman: "I greet you at the beginning of a great career." As Mark Twain opened up the way for the modern American novel, so Whitman opened up the way for modern American poetry.

WOTTON, SIR HENRY (1568–1639) was a diplomat in the service of Elizabeth I and James I, a writer on architecture, and a poet.

Index.